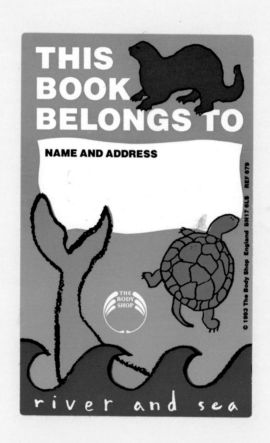

THIS
BOOK
BELONGS TO

NAME AND ADDRESS

© 1993 The Body Shop England BN17 6LS   REF 67B

THE
BODY
SHOP

river and sea

BEARS' BEDTIME STORYBOOK

BEARS' BEDTIME STORYBOOK

STORIES AND POEMS BY

BRENDA APSLEY

MOIRA BUTTERFIELD

GEOFFREY COWAN

JEAN MCKENZIE

KATE MONTAGNON

SALLY SHERINGHAM

ILLUSTRATED BY GRAHAM PERCY

HAMLYN

This edition first published 1989 by
The Hamlyn Publishing Group Limited
Michelin House, 81 Fulham Road, London SW3 6RB

Text and illustrations copyright © 1987 Octopus Books Limited

ISBN 0 600 56783 4

Produced by Mandarin Offset, printed in Hong Kong

GOODNIGHT, JAMIE

Jamie Bear was in bed, but he couldn't go to sleep. He tossed and turned, shook his pillow and pulled the blankets under his chin, but still he couldn't sleep. He looked at the clock. It was late.

Jamie's dad crept into his room. 'Not asleep yet?' he whispered.

'No,' said Jamie. 'I can't sleep. I tried counting sheep, but it didn't work.'

Jamie's dad looked out at the inky-black sky. Stars dotted the blackness. 'Why not try counting stars instead?' he said, and crept outside.

Jamie looked at the twinkling, winking stars and began to count.

'One, two,' he counted, and his eyes felt heavy.

'Three, four,' and he yawned a big yawn.

'Five, six,' and his eyes started to close.

'Seven, eight, nine,' Jamie counted. But before he could say 'Ten,' he was fast asleep.

Jamie's dad peeped in. 'Goodnight, Jamie,' he said.

PLAYTIME

I like dressing up,' said Lucy Bear.
'So do I,' agreed Larry Bear.

They were putting on a play and had borrowed a big basket full of costumes. Larry even wore a false beard.

They had invited all their friends to see the play and their best friend, Bruce Bear, was in charge at the door. Soon, every seat was taken.

When Larry and Lucy arrived at the door, Bruce said: 'No more. Sorry. We're full up!'

'It's *Lucy and me*!' said Larry, lowering his beard.

'Sorry,' chuckled Bruce. 'I didn't recognize you both for a moment! Come on in!'

KEEPING WARM

Brr! I'm freezing!' shivered Patrick Bear, one wintry morning. 'I'll light a fire.'

But when he went to the shed, he saw it was empty.

'Oh, no!' groaned Patrick. 'I'll have to find some more firewood.'

So he put on his hat, boots and thickest coat and set off into the forest. Soon, he spotted a long branch that had broken and was lying on the ground.

'I'll drag that home and make a fire with it,' thought Patrick, picking up one end.

It was hard work. Patrick puffed and pulled until, finally, he reached his garden. Then he fetched a saw and cut the branch into smaller pieces.

'Phew! Finished at last!' he gasped, carrying some firewood indoors. 'But I won't light the fire just yet, after all,' he thought. 'Being so busy has warmed me up nicely.'

WINTER BEAR

Later on that winter's day,
When cold winds blew the sun away,
Patrick lit his cosy fire;
Watched the bright flames leaping higher.
Outside, the snow fell soft and white,
Patrick thought: 'A pretty sight!'
As cosy as a bear could be,
Eating toast and sipping tea.

THE SURPRISE PARCEL

It was Susie's birthday. Her friend Sam arrived with a big parcel wrapped in red paper, tied with a silver ribbon. The parcel was so big Sam could hardly see over it or round it. He set it down. 'Happy birthday, Susie,' he said.

'What is it?' asked Susie.

'Three guesses,' said Sam.

Susie walked round the parcel. It was lumpy and bumpy. 'Is it a big rag doll?' she asked.

'No,' said Sam. 'Guess again.'

Susie took the parcel to see how heavy it was. 'Is it a play house?' she asked.

Sam shook his head. 'No,' he said. 'One guess left.'

Susie felt the parcel carefully. She could feel six long, rounded, bottle shapes and two much smaller round shapes. 'Two balls,' she said, 'and six skittle shapes. That's it — a set of skittles! What a nice surprise parcel.'

SPLAT!

Young Barnaby Bear decided that
He'd like to be an acrobat.
He juggled with spoons and an ice-cream,
It really was a sight to be seen.
Now Barnaby Bear's decided that
His ice-cream cone looks like a clown's hat!

WHAT'S COOKING?

William was watching his dad cooking. 'What are you making?' he asked.

'Wait and see,' said Dad.

William's dad mixed flour and ginger in a bowl, then he melted sugar, butter and treacle on the stove. He added milk and an egg, and stirred till the mixture was very thick and sticky. 'What can it be?' thought William.

William's dad rolled out the mixture and shaped it. He made fat bodies, arms and legs, then added round ears and currant eyes. William watched and smiled. Now he knew. 'Gingerbread bears!' he said. 'Yummy!'

PATRICK AND THE SNOW BEAR

Patrick looked out of his bedroom window and for a moment thought he had woken up in another land. For the lawn, the flowers, the trees and even his swing had turned a brilliant sparkly white.

'It's been snowing!' he shouted excitedly.

As soon as he had finished breakfast Patrick put on his coat, scarf, bobble hat and boots and ran into the garden. The snow made a lovely crisp crunchy sound underfoot, and he left deep footprints wherever he went. What a pity his two best friends, George and Allen, were in bed with mumps; they could have had such fun tracking one another.

After a while Patrick got bored playing in the snow on his own. It wasn't much fun throwing snowballs when you had no one to throw them at, and what was the point of pretending to be a dragon with white fiery breath if there was no one to watch you? He was beginning to feel a bit lonely.

'I know what I'll do,' he said. 'I'll build a Snow Bear!' and he went to find his father's shovel. For the rest of the morning, he moulded and patted and smoothed and sculpted and shaped. Patrick concentrated so hard he forgot all about being lonely.

At last the Snow Bear was finished. What a work of art!

'Now I've got my very own friend to play with!' laughed Patrick. 'I think I'll call you Snowy.' And even though Snowy was made of snow, Patrick swears to this day that, at that moment, he winked at him.

THIRSTY BEAR

Every Monday, at four o'clock, young Brown Bear visited his Grandma. She always had a cup of tea and made him a jug of hot chocolate to drink. But today young Brown Bear was late and the chocolate was getting cold. Suddenly, young Brown Bear raced in, puffing hard.

'I forgot the time, so I ran all the way,' he gasped. 'Now I'm too hot to drink that chocolate.'

'I guessed you would be,' said Grandma. 'So I added some ice to the jug of hot chocolate. Now you can have a nice *iced*-chocolate drink!'

FLYING!

When I grow up I want to be,
A pilot flying high,
I'll visit foreign countries,
And speed across the sky.
But at the moment I must keep
My feet upon the ground,
I'll fly my model aeroplane,
And watch it zoom around.

THE WALK

Patch the dog lay before the open fire, drowsily dreaming of a big, juicy bone.

'Come on, lazy! You can't just sleep all day,' called Arnold Bear. 'You need some exercise. I'll take you for a walk.'

Patch opened one eye, then closed it again, hoping Arnold would go away. After all, it was very warm and cosy indoors.

But Arnold clipped the leash to Patch's collar.

Patch yawned, stretched and followed Arnold out of the front door.

Outside, Patch sniffed the fresh air. It was full of interesting smells. Patch began to walk—faster and faster. In no time, he was running along, happily chasing leaves and pulling Arnold behind him.

'W . . . wait for me!' puffed Arnold, clinging to Patch's leash.

Later, as they returned home, Patch settled comfortably by the fire once more. So did Arnold.

'You took *me* for a walk!' he gasped wearily. 'Now *I* need a rest, too!'

TED'S SWIM

When Ted woke up and looked through the window the sun was shining and the sea sparkled like diamonds.

'Just right for a swim,' he thought.

He collected his swimsuit and goggles and a beach towel but just as he was ready, a big black rain cloud came over the cliff.

'You'll have to wait until that's passed over,' said his mother.

Ted felt very glum and did not know what to do with himself. Then he had an idea. He took out his easel and crayons and drew a picture of the sun and the sea and the cliffs. But he didn't draw the big black cloud.

By the time he had finished, the rain had gone, the sun was shining and, in two minutes, Ted was happily splashing about in the sea.

THE MISSING PANCAKE

Ted was busy making pancakes for supper. First he mixed some flour and eggs in a bowl, then poured the mixture into a pan. After it had cooked on one side Ted threw the pancake up in the air and caught it the other way up. Then he cooked it on the other side. (Only grown-up bears can do this as little bears might get burnt.)

Ted thought that tossing pancakes was great fun. He tossed them higher and higher and at last, one of them didn't come down again. Ted looked up in amazement. There was the pancake, stuck on the lampshade.

He stared in surprise for a minute and suddenly, splosh! down came the pancake right on Ted's head!

EXPLORING!

Three bears were going exploring.

'It's exciting!' said Martin Bear, packing the kitbag and hamper.

'An adventure!' agreed his brother Malcolm, who was wearing a special explorer's hat and carrying the cooking-pots.

'I wonder what we'll discover?' added their brother Michael. He took a huge kettle so they could boil water over a camp fire.

'Let's explore beyond that hill,' said Malcolm.

They walked quickly at first, but soon slowed down.

'It's hard work,' puffed Michael.

'We've so much to carry,' groaned Martin.

Then it began to rain. In no time, the bears were soaked. So was their food, as the hamper leaked.

'We can't light a camp fire,' shivered Michael. 'Everything's too wet!'

The three brothers hurried home. They felt much better after a steaming bath and supper.

'We didn't discover anything,' grumbled Martin.

'Yes, we did,' grinned Michael. 'We discovered that it's *nicer staying at home*!'

TIDY BEAR

Tidy Bear liked to be busy. So he didn't mind doing the housework. He dusted, brushed and vacuumed, until his home was spotless.

When he had finished, he sat down to rest. But soon he was bored.

'What shall I do now?' he wondered.

Outside, the wind howled. Suddenly, a strong gust blew open Tidy's front door. Dust and leaves swept in from the woods.

'I'll have to clean my house all over again,' he thought, locking the door.

'Oh, well,' he whistled happily, 'it gives me something to do!'

SLEEPY BEAR

After every busy day,
Mother Bear sits sewing,
This time it's a patchwork quilt,
Look how much it's growing!
Every night is just the same,
When we come a-peeping,
Mother's sitting in her chair,
But very soon she's sleeping.
For after all her work is done,
Her children tucked in bed,
Mother Bear is tired too,
See her nodding head!

STANLEY'S TREASURE

Stanley Bear went to the seaside with his parents. While Dad sunbathed and his mother set out the picnic, Stanley pulled on some flippers and a snorkel.

He dived into the sea.

'I'll search for sunken treasure,' he thought.

Suddenly, he saw something on the seabed. Covered with mud, it seemed very old. Quickly, he swam back to the beach, carrying it with him.

'Look! Treasure! Is it gold?' he gasped.

His mother took it and smiled. 'No,' she said, 'and it's quite new, really.'

'How can you tell?' frowned Stanley.

'Because it's the bracelet I lost here, last week,' said his mother happily. 'Thank you for finding it for me.'

ALL FALL DOWN

Picking apples from a tree,
Bertie Bear hummed happily.
But Bertie balanced on a stool,
And he forgot that he might fall!
Sure enough the stool has tipped,
And Bertie to the ground has slipped.
Cheer up, Bertie — look around,
Now all the apples are on the ground!

TERENCE GOES FISHING

For his birthday, Terence was given something he had always wanted — a fishing rod. He hurried to a nearby stream, put his bait on the hook, and waited . . . and waited . . . and waited for the rod to give a little twitch.

'I don't think there can be any fish in the stream,' Terence said to his sister sadly at supper. 'Or if there are, they're certainly keeping well away from me.'

'Don't give up quite yet,' said his sister, smiling to herself, for she had just had an idea.

The next day Terence returned to the stream, put his bait on the hook and waited . . . and waited. At last the rod gave a little twitch. His paws trembled with excitement as he wound up the reel . . . but it wasn't a fish at all but a fish cake!

'Oh, well, I suppose a fish cake is the next best thing to a fish,' said Terence, laughing at his sister's joke!

THE SPECIAL SURPRISE

I t was Bessie Bear's birthday. Tom Bear put on his best bow-tie and jacket, and went calling with a present.

'A surprise for you. Happy birthday, Bessie,' he said, when she opened the door.

'Thank you, Tom,' said Bessie. 'I've had such lovely gifts, like chocolates and flowers. I can't think what *you've* brought me!'

'Oh, you've had chocolates already?' asked Tom, looking disappointed. Then he handed Bessie the box which he had gift-wrapped specially.

'It looks beautiful,' said Bessie. 'I wonder what's inside!'

Quickly, she unwrapped the box while Tom watched. But as she lifted the lid, out popped a bright jack-in-the-box.

'Ohhhh!' cried Bessie, looking startled.

'Oh, no!' groaned Tom. 'How did *that* get in there!'

Suddenly, he remembered. Tom's younger brother, Sam, had a box which was just the same size.

'I must have wrapped the *wrong* box, by mistake, before I left home!' he explained to Bessie.

But she just laughed and laughed.

'Why,' smiled Bessie. 'That was the *funniest* birthday surprise I've ever had!'

HELPFUL BEAR

I don't mind helping,
Really, it's true!
I'll wash up the dishes,
Especially for you.
I'll rinse all the glasses,
Scrub all the pans,
Polish the silver,
With my *bear* hands!
Of course I can do it,
Really, I can,
I'm very helpful,
You know that I am!

TEDDY BUNS

Teddy came home from school all hot and bothered. The sun was burning his fur and he felt like a fried egg. He stamped into the kitchen where his mother was baking.

'Hello,' she said. 'What are you so cross about?'

'I'm too *hot*,' said Teddy in a temper and stamped into the living room. 'What's for tea?' he called out.

'Teddy Buns,' replied his mother.

At tea time, Teddy felt a bit ashamed for being so grumpy.

On his plate his mum had put two lovely spicy toasted buttered *hot cross buns*.

PAINTING IS EASY

One day Annabel Bear watched a television programme called 'Painting made Easy'. Someone showed how to paint large pictures, called murals, on doors and walls. Someone else showed how to make a modern-art picture by splashing different coloured paints on to a piece of paper. Then everyone in the studio tried decorating Easter eggs with bright spots, stripes and squiggles.

'Painting is easy. Anyone can be an artist,' said one of the bears on television. Annabel thought that it looked very easy, too. She decided to try out some of the painting ideas straight away.

Annabel collected all kinds of different coloured paints and some brushes. She started to paint the things in her room.

She painted all the chairs but, because this made them wet, she had to sit on the floor.

She tried painting a big mural picture on the door but, because this made it wet, she couldn't open it!

When Annabel had finished, everything except the television was covered with wet paint.

Annabel sat on the floor and waited for the paint to dry. She decided that being an artist was a very messy job. In fact, she looked like a painting herself, because she was covered in coloured splashes like a modern-art painting.

Annabel decided to write to the bears on television, asking them to make a programme called 'Cleaning up'. And she signed the letter with a paint-covered pawprint.

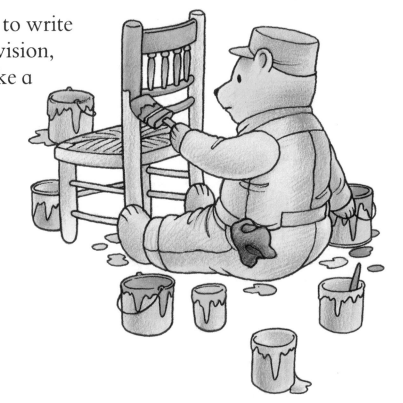

THE QUARREL

Jake and Penny were always quarrelling. Today they were quarrelling about marbles. 'I'll win all your marbles,' said Jake. 'You'll have none left.'

'No, you won't,' said Penny.
'Yes, I will,' said Jake.
Penny rolled a marble hard. 'I'll win all *your* marbles,' she said.
'Right!' shouted Jake. 'We'll play right now! I'll win, I'll show you.'
Just then their mother arrived. She picked up all the marbles. 'No, you won't,' she said. 'I'm tired of your arguing. The game's over — and so is the quarrel. Come on, it's time to eat.'

BIRTHDAY BEAR

Today is Bertram's birthday,
He's as excited as can be,
With lots and lots of presents,
Now it's his birthday tea!
His friends sing: 'Happy birthday!'
They cheer and jump about,
As Bertram takes a deep breath,
And blows the candles out.
'What a special day,' he says,
'It's one that I adore.
I'm birthday bear. Hooray! Hooray!
Look at me. I'm *four*!'

ROSEMARY'S EXOTIC HAT

Rosemary Bear loved wearing exotic hats covered in ribbons and bows and lace and tassels and frills and net — you name it, Rosemary had worn it!

But now she wanted a particularly exotic one to wear to her daughter's wedding. So she covered her old straw hat with flowers. My, what an exotic hat! The only trouble was, the bees thought so, too. Wherever the hat went, the bees followed.

So Rosemary covered the hat instead with fruit. My, what an exotic hat! The only trouble was, the wasps thought so, too. Wherever the hat went, the wasps followed.

'Oh, dear, what am I going to do?' thought Rosemary. And then she had another idea…

The wedding guests had never seen a hat covered in *vegetables* before! My, what an exotic hat! And what a piece of luck for Rosemary that the caterpillars hadn't spotted it!

BETTY'S BUBBLES

One morning, Betty was clearing out an old cupboard when she found a dirty old clay pipe.

'This could do with a wash,' she said and filled a bowl with water and washing-up liquid and gave the pipe a good scrub.

'But how do I dry *inside* the pipe?' she wondered as she gently blew the water out. To her surprise an enormous bubble came from the other end of the pipe. It sparkled and shone and floated up in the air. Then it popped!

'How lovely,' thought Betty. 'I would like to see another.'

She dipped the pipe into the water and blew gently again. This time, two bubbles came floating up in the air.

Betty forgot all about the cleaning. She sat on the floor with the pipe and her bowl and blew bubbles all morning.

'This is more fun than housework,' said a rather damp but very happy Betty Bear.

DOUGHNUT RINGS

Becky Bear liked playing 'rings', throwing small hoops over a little peg.

'Grandpa's coming today,' she thought. 'I'll cook him some doughnut rings, his favourites.'

But when Grandpa was late, Becky went to find him. She saw him on the far side of the stream between the houses.

'The bridge is down,' he called, waving his walking-stick. 'I can't cross the stream.'

'You can still have your afternoon treat,' said Becky, and she went to fetch the doughnuts.

'Hold up your walking-stick,' she said. One by one, she threw the doughnuts which landed over the end of the walking-stick.

Grandpa chuckled.

'Just like playing "rings",' smiled Becky.

SWEET SUSIE

Teddy fell in love,
With little Susie Bear.
'Soon she will be four,' he said,
'And I'm invited there.
I must take a gift,
Dear me, what shall it be?
I know just the very thing.
Some candies made by me!'

THE BEAR FAMILY'S CHRISTMAS

Great Grandfather Bear lived alone in a big old house. He thought Christmas was the best time of the year, a special time when families should be together. So every year the whole Bear family — and it was a big one — travelled from far and near to spend the holiday together at Great Grandfather's house.

Right in the middle of the big old house was a tall hallway. It was here that Great Grandfather Bear put up the biggest Christmas tree you ever saw.

Last Christmas Eve Great Grandfather Bear was still decorating the tree when the rest of the family — aunts and uncles, brothers and sisters, mothers and fathers, nephews and nieces — all went up to bed. 'I'll stay and finish the tree,' he said. 'When it's done I'll know Christmas is really here. You can all come and put your gifts around the tree first thing in the morning.'

Soon the big old house was dark and quiet. William, the youngest great-grandson, lay in his bed and waited and waited. Then he slid out of bed and, still in his pyjamas, crept downstairs. He wanted his presents to be the first ones around the Christmas tree.

What a surprise William got when he opened the door of the big hall! The room was full of aunts and uncles, brothers and sisters, mothers and fathers, nephews and nieces — the whole Bear family! They were still in pyjamas and nightgowns, and they carried gifts of all shapes and sizes.

'I wanted to be the first to put my presents under the tree,' William explained.

'So did we,' said the others. 'Looks like we all had the same idea.'

Great Grandfather Bear hung the last lights on the tree and climbed down the ladder. He looked at his pocket watch. 'It's just past twelve o'clock,' he said. 'Merry Christmas, everyone.'

'Merry Christmas,' said the Bear family. 'Merry Christmas, William.'

A SURPRISE PARTY

The bears were watching a banquet on television.

'I would so love to go out all dressed up and be waited on,' sighed Betty.

Bimbo and Biffy put their heads together, then told Betty to go and dress herself up.

Meanwhile they cleared a space in the outhouse and hung coloured paper round the walls. They made a box into a table and put on it a glass with two straws in. While Bimbo was mixing some fruit juice in a shaker, Biffy put some fruit on a toothpick to make a cocktail decoration. Then they went to fetch Betty. They fussed around her as though they were waiters and Betty sat down at the table, elegantly sipping her special drink.

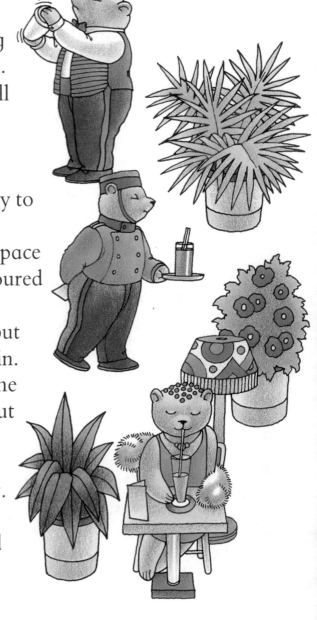

It's true that the two boy bears dropped things and bumped into one another, and that nothing was quite as exotic as the banquet they had seen on television, but everyone had great fun, especially Betty.

PUDDING

Bears love pudding good and hot,
Sweet and sticky in the pot.
It's a favourite thing to eat,
At any meal — a tasty treat.
When Mother Bear calls 'Pudding time',
Her family's waiting in a line,
Table laid — spoons at the ready,
Pudding fit for any Teddy!

THE PICNIC PLACE

One fine day Bright Bear put on her beach robe, packed a picnic, and went to the seaside.

'I like the sun!' she thought.

Meanwhile, Country Bear put on her hat and walking-shoes and set off for the woods.

'I like the shade!' she thought.

But the beach was too hot and the woods were too cool. Both bears were heading back home, when they met each other.

'I know where we can picnic together!' said Country Bear. Soon, they sat in her garden, which overlooked the sea. There was a big tree beside them.

'We've sunshine *and* shade here!' they smiled.

HUM FOR YOUR SUPPER

B uster and his brothers had a music group and were really rather good. Bruno played the guitar and the others sang. Their favourite place to practise was in the country, so they would often take a basket of food and stay out all day.

One day, they were out practising when the most delicious smell of fried onions and steak floated towards them across the fields.

'Oh my!' said Boris, 'just smell that.'

They could see a car parked by some trees not far away. The lovely smell was coming from near there.

It was a family of bears: Mr and Mrs Bear and their very small twins. The twins could hear Buster and his brothers playing, and wanted to go over to them.

'No,' said Mrs Bear, 'they are big bears. They won't want you.'

Mr Bear was busy with a barbecue, turning the steak over and humming to himself. The charcoal grew hotter and hotter and the smell more and more delicious. The four bears in the field were looking longingly towards the barbecue.

'Do you think they might ask us to supper?' asked Bernard.

'No,' said Buster. 'We can't intrude.'

So, although all the bears wanted to meet each other, it looked as if no one would make the first move. Bruno's tummy started to rumble. His brothers could hear it. They could also hear something else. It was Mr Bear humming as he turned the steaks on the grill.

Softly, Bruno began to strum his guitar in time to the humming; the brothers joined in until they were all humming the same tune as Mr Bear.

'Listen,' said the twins. 'You'll have to talk to them *now*. They're playing for us.'

'All right,' said Mrs Bear, 'run across and ask them to supper.'

The twins scampered across the field and in no time at all the four hungry brothers were tucking into tasty hamburgers.

'This must be what you call humming for your supper,' said Bruno happily, taking another bite.

A BIRTHDAY CAROL

I t was a snowy Christmas Eve and the carol singers were visiting all the houses. Nearby, Binkie trudged along in the snow pulling her sledge and thinking about all the others at home getting ready for the Christmas party.

She felt miserable. It was her birthday and with all the fuss about Christmas, nobody seemed to be taking any notice of her. Two tears slid down her face and wet her fur. She wiped them away with her glove and tried to cheer up. She must not spoil the party just because they had all forgotten it was her birthday.

When she arrived home she washed her face and got ready for the party.

It was a lovely party. All the bears were there except the twins.

'Where are Bertie and Brenda?' said Binkie.

'They are out carol singing,' said Tiny Ted, 'and they're going to — Ooops!'

He did not finish what he was going to say because Biffy put a paw over his mouth. Just then, Binkie heard carol singers outside. It was the twins. They were singing a carol she had not heard before.

All the bears stopped talking and looked at her. Tiny Ted's eyes nearly popped out of his head. He couldn't wait any longer.

'It's your birthday carol,' he shouted. 'The twins have written it specially for you.'

Birthday greetings Binkie Bear
And love from all we bring you.
To let you know that we all care
A special song we sing you.
Although we've been such busy bears,
We hope you didn't thinkie
That we'd forgotten that it was
The birthday of our Binkie.

Then everyone crowded round Binkie to wish her happy birthday.

'We had to say "thinkie" to make it rhyme with Binkie,' said the twins. 'We hope you liked it.'

'It was perfect,' said Binkie.

PUDDLES

I wonder if, like Patti Bear,
You love puddles, too?
The very deep and muddy ones,
When only boots will do!
For she pretends she's far away,
In the jungle heat,
With fearsome, scaly crocodiles,
Swimming round her feet!
Or, dreamily, she's paddling,
On a desert isle,
In crystal-clear blue waters,
Sand stretching for a mile,
But Patti's in a muddle,
It's plain as plain can be,
She's standing in a puddle,
Nowhere near the sea!

MY FRIEND TED

My best friend is a teddy bear,
Ted's old and worn, but I don't care.
Because, you see, he likes to play
With me at any time of day.
Ted sits beside me at each meal,
He always knows just how I feel.
And when it's time to go to bed,
I always sleep beside old Ted!

A TASTY CAKE

Ted was an untidy cook, and one day he decided to bake a cake.

'This is going to taste really good,' said Ted as he broke some eggs into the bowl. 'Ooops!' he said, as he missed and they fell on the table. What a mess!

The next time he aimed straight and began to beat the mixture.

'Mmm,' he said as he tried some. 'This tastes *really* good.'

He went on adding ingredients then trying a bit more.

'This tastes *really* good,' he kept saying.

He said it so often that when it was time to bake the cake there was none left. He had eaten it all up!

TED TO THE RESCUE

Ted was a very good swimmer. He could dive from the highest board and stay underwater longer than any other bear. He was the champion at the bears' open-air pool at the seaside.

Sometimes, when he was ready to dive, he would look across at the water-skiers and wish he could have a try. But he had no boat and didn't know anyone he could ask to pull him along.

'Come on Ted, stop day-dreaming,' the other bears would shout, and watch him dive head-first into the water.

Mrs Bear and Belinda came almost every day to watch Ted. Ted thought Belinda looked a lonely little bear. She was very shy and carried a doll with her everywhere she went. Belinda and her mother used to shiver when Ted made his splendid dives. They seemed to think he was very brave.

One day, Ted was paddling in the sea and watching the water-skiers. How he wished he could have a try himself. He saw that Mrs Bear and Belinda were splashing about in the sea. As usual, Belinda had her doll with her.

Suddenly, a huge wave came rolling towards them.

'Look out!' called Ted.

They looked up and began to run back to the shore. The wave seemed to chase them, but Mrs Bear pulled her daughter to safety. In the struggle, the doll was swept out of Belinda's paw.

'Oh my doll, my doll,' cried Belinda, 'save her, somebody.'

She tried to go back into the sea but Mrs Bear held on to her. Ted coolly waded in and swam about until he found the doll. He shook off the water and shyly gave it to Belinda.

'Thank you, thank you,' she said. 'However can we repay you?'

'It was nothing,' grinned Ted. 'Please don't bother about it.'

Belinda whispered something to her mother, and Mrs Bear said, 'We have hired a speedboat for the holiday. Would you like to come for a ride?'

'A speedboat,' said Ted excitedly. 'Oooh, I would love to come water-skiing with you.'

For the rest of the holiday, Ted went water-skiing every day with Mrs Bear, his new friend, Belinda, and, of course, the doll in her dried-out clothes.

FLYING HIGH

Stanley Bear had two kites.

'I wonder which will fly higher?' he thought, one windy day.

First, he tried his new box-kite. Up and up it soared. Then he flew his old pink and blue kite. It danced and whizzed about, its bright tail flapping in the breeze.

'Hmm,' wondered Stanley. 'It's hard to tell.'

Suddenly the string broke and a strong gust swept away the pink and blue kite, until it was a tiny spot high in the sky.

At last the wind dropped, and so did Stanley's kite.

'No doubt about it now,' grinned Stanley. 'My old kite went the highest!'

WHO'S THERE, BEAR?

When we were in bed, the telephone rang,
It gave us such a terrible fright.
It was Uncle Jim in Australia,
He'd forgotten that here it was night.
'I have just called to say hello,' he said,
'I am sorry the time's not quite right.
I wanted to ask how you're getting on,
I suppose I'd do better to write.'

WILLIAM AND THE APPLES

W hat was William up to? He was a lazy bear who never did anything for anyone unless there was something in it for him. And now he had offered to spend Saturday picking Winifred Bear's apples for her. And he wasn't just picking the easy ones; he was standing at the top of the ladder and stretching for the high-up ones, too.

'He must be stealing them,' Winifred muttered to herself. But no, his pockets were too small for apples, and there was nowhere else he could hide them.

'You must be turning over a new leaf, William,' she shouted.

William looked down at her and just smiled. He wasn't going to remind her that her garden backed on to the football stadium, and that the reason he was picking apples was so he could have a grandstand view of the match for free!

TED HAS HIS NECK SCRUBBED

When Ted finished his push-ups one day his mother noticed he wasn't wearing the chain he usually had round his neck.

'Was it there when you washed your neck this morning?' she asked.

'Oh, er, I forgot to wash it this morning,' said Ted, and tried to think where he might have lost the chain.

'Go and do your piano practice,' said Mother. 'You haven't done any for a week.'

Ted went over to the piano and there, right on top of the piano stool, was the chain. He showed it to his mother and said, 'It must have been there all week!'

'In that case,' his mother said, 'you can't have washed your neck for a week or you would have noticed you weren't wearing the chain!'

She hauled Ted off to the bathroom and scrubbed his neck clean till it was sore. Poor Ted never forgot to wash it again!

JAKE TAKES A PICTURE

Jessie was a quiet, sweet-tempered little bear, who usually let her brother Jake have all his own way. One day he wanted to take a picture of her for a photographic competition.

'Go and put on some dungarees,' he said.

'No,' said Jessie. 'I'm a pretty bear and I want the picture to show me as I am.'

'It's much better my way,' said Jake.

'I'll do it my way or I won't do it at all,' said Jessie, nicely but firmly. So, for once, Jake had to agree.

This is the picture Jake took. Do you think Jessie was right?

THE BEST BIT OF THE CAKE

Daddy Bear and Thomas were making a fruit cake. They put flour, eggs, spices, sugar and fruit into a big mixing bowl and stirred it with a wooden spoon. Then they baked it in the oven.

When the cake was cooked, Daddy Bear added layers of yellow marzipan, white icing, cream swirls and chocolate shapes.

The cake was finished. 'Which bit do you like best?' asked Daddy. 'The fruit cake, the marzipan, the icing, the cream or the chocolate?'

'None of those things,' said Thomas. 'The bit I like best is licking the spoon.'

BRENDA'S NOTEPAD

Brenda Bear woke up and looked at the notepad by her bed. If there was anything she had to remember, she always wrote it on the pad. CLEAN THE HOUSE, she read. 'Oh,' sighed Brenda, 'I forgot about that.' Brenda wrote another note on the pad, then went to the kitchen.

With mops and buckets, brooms and dusters, Brenda scrubbed and polished and brushed her house all morning. Then she went back to her notepad and read another note. 'Oh,' she thought. 'I forgot about that.'

Brenda put on her beach clothes and went out, carrying her air-bed, snorkel and flippers. She was smiling.

What was written on the notepad? SWIMMING!

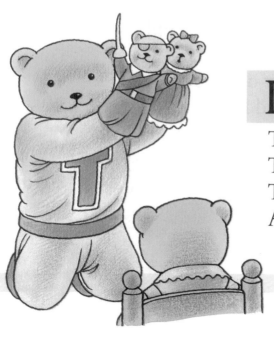

THE PUPPET SHOW

I wondered what to do today;
I felt really bored and low.
Then Mother had a good idea:
To put on a puppet show.
The play's about a lady fair
And a pirate — yo, ho, ho!

LEAPFROG

Rachel and Ronald didn't have a garden, so they often played on a patch of earth outside Mrs De Bear's dark, old-fashioned house. Mrs De Bear dressed all in black and Rachel and Ronald were sure she was a witch.

'Go away, you horrible children,' she would shout, waving her black rolled-up umbrella. 'Go away, and leave me in peace.' Rachel and Ronald always ran off before she could cast a spell on them. One day Rachel and Ronald were playing happily outside Mrs De Bear's house. They thought she was asleep or out shopping, because she hadn't yet shouted at them. Rachel leapfrogged over Ronald, and went so high that she could see through Mrs De Bear's window. And there she saw the black, rolled-up umbrella waving, but no Mrs De Bear! 'I think she's signalling for help!' said Rachel. 'Come on.'

Now wasn't the time to worry about Mrs De Bear being a witch, about being turned into frogs or put in a pot and boiled up for dinner. This was an emergency! Taking a deep breath, they rushed into the house.

Mrs De Bear was lying on the floor with a broken leg. Rachel and Ronald phoned for an ambulance.

A few days later, Mrs De Bear was back at home with her leg in plaster. 'And to think, my dears, if you hadn't been playing outside I could have lain there for days,' she said, beaming at Rachel and Ronald. 'Now, what can I give you as a reward? Ah! Perhaps you would like to look through my dressing-up box. I used to be an actress, so I have lots of costumes.'

What fun they had trying on all the different clothes. Some were very exotic. They even put on a song-and-dance routine for Mrs De Bear, who cried with laughter. 'My dears, you've brought back such lovely memories of my past. You've made a lonely old bad-tempered bear very happy. You must come and play here whenever you like.' And so they did. It was much more fun than playing leapfrog on the patch of earth.

'And we thought she was a witch!' said Rachel.

'You should never judge a bear by what he wears,' laughed Ronald wearing a wizard's hat, a swirly black cloak and a false moustache.

ODD EGG

M y serve!' said Jake Bear. He was playing table-tennis with his sister, Jessie. Jake hit the ball extra hard. It bounced off the table, past Jessie, and into the kitchen.

Mrs Bear was making a cake. Her electric mixer was noisy, so she did not hear the ball.

'I'll add the last egg to my cake mix now,' she thought, reaching into the open egg-box beside her.

'What a strange egg!' she gasped.

'That's my table-tennis ball,' said Jake, peering round the door. 'Of all the places for it to land.'

'Lucky *I* didn't mistake an egg for our ball,' laughed Jake. 'That would have been messy!'

PIRATE PETER

D o come and join our barbecue,'
Says Pirate Peter Bear.
'We've lots of food for you to eat,
And everybody's there!
Hot hamburgers and beefburgers,
And mushrooms on a stick,
Already cooked and sizzling,
Come now and take your pick!
This really is the way to eat,
It's very much more fun,
To have a meal out-of-doors,
While sitting in the sun!'

Blind Bears' Buff

Betty had been trying to give Ted a kiss all Christmas. She knew that if you stand under a piece of mistletoe someone is supposed to kiss you. Betty kept standing under it, but Ted pretended not to notice and took good care not to stand under any mistletoe himself.

Then the time came for Blind Bears' Buff. Ted had a handkerchief tied round his eyes and was trying to catch other bears.

'Now's my chance,' thought Betty.

She stood still under the mistletoe and let Ted catch her. Ted whipped off the hanky to see who he had caught. He was surprised when he saw that *he* was the one who had been caught.

He gave Betty a nice Christmas kiss. The other bears laughed and clapped and, really, Ted didn't seem to mind at all.

COOKERY SCHOOL

Bruno was a greedy bear. He loved food. 'I'm going to cookery school,' he said, 'then I can eat all day long.'

On the first morning Bruno and the other pupils lined up to show the teacher what they were going to cook. The first bear had rice, the second bear cabbages, and the third bear a big pumpkin. Then came Bruno carrying a very heavy basket of potatoes. The other bears had carrots, onions, tomatoes, bottled plums, flour and apples.

All day long the bears peeled and chopped, sliced

and mixed, boiled and baked. Bruno felt very tired.

At the end of a long day the bears lined up again so that the teacher could taste what they had cooked.

One bear carried a stew, another soup, then came fruit, a pink pudding, apple cake, carrot cake, pumpkin pie, plum cake and a casserole. And who was at the end of the line? Bruno, with a heavy bowl of mashed potato.

It was late when he got home. 'What would you like to eat?' asked his mother.

Bruno groaned and pulled a face. 'Ugh!' he said. 'Don't mention food. I never want to eat again!'

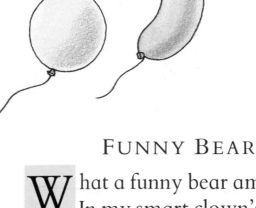

FUNNY BEAR

W hat a funny bear am I,
In my smart clown's clothes,
I don't need a painted mouth,
Or a bright-red nose.
For I have some big balloons,
Come and watch them fly,
Dancing through the air they'll go,
You'll laugh as they float by!

GUESS WHO?

I t was Christmas, and young Brown Bear had
been invited to a fancy-dress party.

'H'mm! What can I go as?' he thought.

At last, he had a good idea. 'Of course!' he said,
hurrying off to find his mother. Soon, she helped him to
make a bright red suit, a cap with a white bobble on
top, and a woolly beard to wear round his chin.

When he arrived at the party, his
friend came to the door, and said:
'I know who you're meant to be...
you're Santa Claus!'

'Not quite,' laughed young
Brown Bear. 'I'm Santa *Paws*!'

GARDENER FRED

Fred Bear lived in a big city, but his favourite pastime was walking in the local park. He loved to see the bright flowers, the leafy bushes and the neat green grass. In fact, he thought he would like to be a gardener very much.

But Fred didn't have a garden of his own. His home was three floors up from the ground. So Fred made himself a windowbox, which he hung outside his bedroom window. He filled it with as many plants as he could. He learnt which were the best ones to grow, and when to water and feed them. After a while he became quite a gardening expert.

Soon there was no more room in Fred's windowbox for any more plants. So he went back to the park, and told the park-keeper all that he had learnt. The park-keeper was very impressed, and asked Fred if he'd like to become a gardener. So now when Fred walks through the park he is usually mowing the neat green grass, and all the flowers and bushes he sees, he has grown himself!

THE AFTER-CHRISTMAS PARTY

When it gets cold, bears get sleepy. Sometimes in the winter they sleep for days and days.

One snowy December, Small Bear slept for a whole week. The only trouble was — he missed Christmas! When he woke up he was very unhappy.

'No presents!' he thought sadly, 'and I've missed the Bears' Party at Big's. What am I going to do with all the cakes I made?'

Just then the telephone rang. It was Big.

'Have you been asleep, Small?' he asked.

'Yes,' said Small. 'I'm sorry I missed the party.'

'You haven't!' boomed Big. 'I was asleep, too, and so was everyone else. We're having the party today instead. Can you come?'

'Yes, please!' shouted Small.

He packed the cakes on to his sledge and set off.

It was the best Christmas party the bears had ever had — even if it was three days late!

Mr Simpkins's Christmas

Everything other bears love about Christmas, Mr Simpkins hated. He didn't like turkey, presents, carols, holly, crackers or paper hats. His idea of a perfect Christmas was sitting in his favourite armchair, eating a hamburger and watching television on his own. Although he was always pleased to see his grandchildren, Kate and Joe, at Christmas he really preferred a quiet life.

One particular Christmas seemed worse than ever. The crackers were noisier, his grandchildren were naughtier, the turkey took hours to cook and the plum pudding caught fire! Kate banged her new drum until she grew bored with it and Joe sulked because he hadn't been given a Superbear outfit. Poor Mr Simpkins went to rest in his favourite armchair.

Straight away Mr Simpkins jumped up again like a jack-in-the-box. Someone had left a piece of holly in his favourite chair! He looked cross for a moment and then saw that Kate and Joe were laughing at their practical joke. Mr Simpkins had to laugh too — imagine being caught out by such a simple trick! At last everyone felt in the party mood, so they spent the rest of Christmas playing all kinds of tricks and games.

Perhaps Christmas wasn't so bad after all!

DIY TED

The bears were going camping.

'I'm not sleeping in a leaky tent!' said Ted.

So he bought a ready-made little wooden shed and took it with him in his van.

Biffy and Bimbo thought this was very funny. When they had pitched their tent they went off to enjoy themselves, leaving Ted to mend some loose boards in the shed. He was just hammering in the last nail when they came back, still laughing.

When it got dark, the bears all went off to bed. Biffy and Bimbo were still laughing at Ted as they crawled into their little tent.

But in the middle of the night there was a terrible storm and the rain poured and poured. Soon it began to leak through the tent, and dripped on to Biffy and Bimbo. They got so wet that Ted let them shelter in his dry wooden shed.

'Who's laughing now?' Ted said.

FEED THE BIRDS

D o you like to feed the birds,
   Just like Bernice Bear?
Can you see them by her boots?
How many birds are there?
When they all fly down to her,
She says, 'Come and see,
I've breadcrumbs from my breakfast,
And cake crumbs saved from tea!'

FEELING HUNGRY

I t was a cold day. Bernice Bear peered out of the
   window and saw lots of birds sitting about.
They had fluffed out their feathers to keep warm and
they didn't look very happy.

'They look hungry,' thought Bernice. So she put on
her hat and went to buy some wild-bird seed.

It was quite a long walk home. But when Bernice
got back, the birds were still there. She changed
into her boots, as the garden was very wet.

'Here you are,' she called, sprinkling seed
on to the grass. The birds swooped down
and ate it.

Then Bernice walked into the woods and
threw down more food for the birds there.

'That was hungry work,' she thought,
as she left. 'I've fed the birds. Now I'll
feed me!'

SUSAN'S BIRTHDAY

Susan woke with a feeling in her tummy; the sort of feeling when you know today is different from other days. And then she remembered. It was her birthday! She got up and crept into the dining-room to look at her presents. But where were they? She looked in the sitting-room and the kitchen and even the garage. Not a sniff of a present! 'They must have forgotten it's my birthday,' thought Susan.

After breakfast, her mother said they were going to Granny's.

'I don't want to go,' said Susan sulkily, but eventually her mother managed to persuade her. And there, on Granny's dining-room table, was the biggest, most inviting-looking pile of presents Susan had ever seen!

'Bet you thought we'd forgotten your birthday,' laughed her brother Jim.

Susan was already busy opening her surprise birthday presents, so she just answered with a very happy smile.

TEDDY BEARS' PICNIC

Sally and Ian had won a singing competition. As a reward Mr Jones, their music teacher, took them for a picnic. But they weren't getting on very fast. Every time Mr Jones saw something that reminded him of a song, he would play it on his guitar and Sally and Ian would have to sing. When they walked up a hill he played *Jack and Jill*, when they passed some sheep he played *Little Bo-Peep* and when they passed a well he played *Ding Dong Bell*. It was nearly dark when, at last, they got to the picnic spot, and Ian and Sally were famished.

'Now, children, we'll have one more song before we eat,' said Mr Jones. Sally nearly said, 'We have to sing for our supper, do we?' but managed to stop herself, because Mr Jones would have made them sing *Little Tommy Tucker*!

I expect you can guess what they did sing. Yes, it was the *Teddy Bears' Picnic*! At last!

THE DISAPPEARING CAKE

The bears were enjoying Biffy's birthday party when, suddenly, the lights went out. When they came on again, one of the cakes had disappeared. Someone had hidden it.

'It wasn't me,' said Barbara. 'I was giving Bertie some potato salad when the lights went out.'

'And I was pouring out some orange juice for Betty,' said Bernard.

'I was talking to Bertie,' said Boris.

'I was putting ketchup on my hamburger,' said Billy.

'I was just going to eat some cake,' said Bertram.

'I was sitting with my balloon, thinking what a nice

party it was,' said Bimbo sadly.

All the bears were making such a noise that Binkie could not explain that *she* knew where the cake was!

At last all the bears stopped talking.

'I know who took the cake,' said Binkie, finally. 'It was Biffy!'

'Oh dear,' said Biffy, turning quite pink.

All the bears looked at him with curiosity.

'I'm sorry,' he said. 'It is my favourite, chocolate cake, and I wanted to eat it all by myself!' Without anyone noticing, he had switched out the lights, so that he could hide it.

'I'm sorry for being so greedy. I won't do it again,' said Biffy — as he cut a big slice of cake for everyone.

ROBERT BEAR GOES ON HOLIDAY

R obert Bear was going on holiday. He packed his big bag carefully and was going to close it when he said, 'Have I packed my toothbrush?' He couldn't remember, so he unpacked the bag. Out came shorts and jeans, sunglasses and shoes until — right at the bottom — he found his toothbrush.

Robert packed his bag again, then said, 'Did I pack my swimsuit?' Out came coats and shirts, socks and hankies until — right at the bottom — he found his swimsuit.

Robert closed the bag. 'Phew,' he said. 'After all that I *need* a holiday.' And off he went.

TEDDY'S TUMMY ACHE

T eddy said, 'I'm feeling quite funny.
I've got a pain inside my tummy.'
The doctor looked at Teddy in bed,
And when he'd seen him quietly said,
'I know why you've got a tummy ache —
It's a simple case of TOO MUCH CAKE!'

THE OLD TRUNK

I t's too cold to play outside today,' said Bertie Bear. 'There's snow everywhere, the pond is covered in ice, and I've got nothing to do.'

'Come and help me,' said his mother. 'I'm busy emptying this old trunk.'

Bertie watched as his mother opened the trunk. She pulled out a big straw hat, a lamp, and lots of dusty books. Then Bertie spotted something much more interesting. 'Whose are these?' he asked as he pulled out some old ice-skates.

'They belonged to your father when he was young,' said Bertie's mother. Then she smiled at him and asked, 'Are you thinking what I'm thinking?'

Bertie smiled back. 'Yes,' he said. 'Now I'm glad the pond is frozen — because I'm going ice-skating!'

And that's just what he did!

WISE OLD WILLIAM

William, Lucy and James had been out shopping, and on the way home Lucy went into a bric-a-brac store. She looked around for so long that William was afraid they would miss the bus.

'We've plenty of time,' said Lucy. She had her eye on an enormous striped umbrella, but when she finally decided to buy it the bus had gone.

'See what you've done!' said James crossly as they started walking home.

They were almost home when it suddenly began to rain. Lucy whipped open the umbrella and they all sat under it until the shower had passed.

'There you are,' said Lucy triumphantly. 'Aren't you glad I bought it?'

William thought to himself, 'If she hadn't made us miss the bus we would have been home before it rained.' But he knew that sometimes, for the sake of peace, it is a wise thing for a bear not to say what a bear is thinking!

LOST IN THE WOODS

Bimbo and Biffy were off for a day in the woods. They hadn't gone far when Bimbo's lunch-box flew open and out fell all his food.

'I told you to have the catch mended,' said Biffy crossly. 'You'll have to share my food now.'

The bears enjoyed their day out (except they were both a bit hungry). But when it was time to go home they could not find the way.

'I think it's this path,' said Biffy.

'No, I think it's this one,' said Bimbo.

'We seem to be lost,' said Biffy in a very small voice.

Suddenly, Bimbo saw something lying on a different path altogether. It was part of the lunch he had dropped.

'Biffy,' he cried, 'this is the way we came.'

So the bears took that path and were soon safely back home.

Before the bears next went out for the day, Bimbo mended his lunch-box and Biffy bought a map showing *all* the paths through the woods.

THE SECRET PLAN

It was very early in the morning. Thomas Bear shook his father awake. 'Wake up,' he whispered.

'What is it?' said Father, still half asleep.

'Ssssh,' said Thomas. 'Have you forgotten our secret plan?'

Father smiled. 'I remember now,' he said. 'Come on.'

Together they tiptoed to the kitchen. Father boiled an egg and made some tea, and Thomas carefully buttered some toast. Father laid a tray, and Thomas added a tiny vase with a flower in it. Then he added a white envelope with MOTHER written on it.

They crept quietly into the bedroom. Thomas's mother was still sleeping. Thomas shook her gently till she opened her eyes and smiled. 'What's this?' she said when she saw the tray Father was carrying.

'It's our secret plan,' said Thomas. 'Breakfast in bed. Happy Mother's Day!'

BATHTIME

When Barnaby Bear took a bath
It used to make him cry,
For when he had to wash his fur,
The soap got in his eye!

But now he finds his daily wash
A much more pleasant task,
Since his dad has lent him
His great big snorkelling mask!

THE MOUNTAIN

James and Tim set off to climb a high mountain
one day. James carried a huge rucksack on his
back.

'What's inside?' asked Tim.

'Wait and see,' said James.

They climbed up, up, up, up,
until they got right to the top of
the mountain. It was very high,
and they could see for miles.

Tim took sandwiches and fruit
from his rucksack, but when
James opened his, he took out —
a camera and a tripod!

'I'm going to take a
photograph to remind us
of the day we climbed the
mountain,' said James. 'Smile please!'

STEPPING STONES

I bet I can run along that path without stepping off the paving stones!' said Jessie Bear to her brother, Jake, as they played in the park.

'I bet I can, too!' replied Jake.

They like to have competitions.

Jessie went first. But she wobbled on one foot and landed on the grass. Then Jake had a go. He soon trod on the grass, as well. So they went to try again.

Suddenly they saw a huge, strange face behind them. They didn't realize it was only a fancy-dress mask.

'Run!' shouted Jake.

They raced along the path together, leaping from one stone to the next.

'It's only me!' called their friend, Patrick Bear. 'I wanted to show you this mask I made.'

Jessie and Jake laughed.

'At least we didn't step off the path that time,' said Jake.

PATRICK'S PUMPKIN

P atrick Bear grew a pumpkin. It was so heavy, he could hardly carry it. So he pushed it along in his wheelbarrow.

It was so big, it won first prize at the pumpkin show. Patrick felt very proud.

Soon, lots of friends came to see his famous pumpkin.

'You're so clever to have grown it!' said one visitor.

'It's enormous!' added another.

'What will you do with it?' asked a third bear.

Patrick glanced around the crowded room, then had an idea.

'I'll show you!' he grinned. 'Come back tomorrow.'

By the next day he had baked the biggest pumpkin pie his friends had ever seen. Patrick gave them all a large slice.

'This is the best way for everyone to enjoy my pumpkin!' he laughed.

His friends agreed. 'It's *delicious*!'

JANE'S PRESENT

Mrs Jane Bear stood at the sink. A tear splashed into the washing-up water. It was her birthday, and she had set her heart on a shiny red handbag. But what had her husband Jim given her? A feather duster! Jim often liked to tease Jane, but she didn't think this was very funny.

'He can't love me any more,' she thought sadly. 'For you would never give someone you love a feather duster.' And another tear plopped into the water.

'Hello, darling,' said a voice behind her. It was Jim, with a flower in his buttonhole and a present under each arm. 'The feather duster was just a joke,' he said. 'Here are your proper presents.'

One was Jane's favourite perfume and the other was . . . yes, the shiny red handbag.

What a happy birthday it had turned out to be!

BEN GOES CAMPING

B en was going camping for the very first time. He pitched his tent at the edge of a wood. He felt rather nervous. It was very dark and very cold, and there were sinister rustling sounds coming from the wood — who knew what was lurking there? Just say a ferocious wolf were to gobble him up in the night, or a ravenous bird were to peck off his nose, or a fierce...

'Don't be such a baby,' said Ben out loud. 'As soon as I light the camp fire I shall be quite safe. Wild animals are afraid of fire.'

Once the cheerful flames started to crackle and flicker, Ben felt much happier. He hung a pot of baked beans over the fire, held out his paws to warm them, and whistled to drown any rustling noises.

'Maybe camping isn't so bad after all,' he laughed. 'In fact I could even get to like the outdoor life!'

GETTING THE BETTER OF BUSTER

Buster was a very large bear with an appetite to match. But Ted thought he was just greedy. One day, to make him look silly, Ted baked an enormous burger bun, filled it, and took it round to Buster's house.

A crowd of bears followed him and saw Buster come out to meet Ted.

'I've brought you a little snack,' said Ted cheekily.

'Thanks,' said Buster. A grin came over his face as he felt the bun. It was as hard as iron. 'Just what I've been looking for. The door of my shed is sticking.'

Buster held the long bun under his arm and ran for the door. He rammed the bun against it and it burst open. How the bears laughed. Every time they saw Ted afterwards they called, 'Baked any good buns lately?' He never tried to get the better of Buster again.

A Private Munch

It's great to sit out in the garden
Enjoying a private munch,
But it bothers a guy
When a passing fly
Brings four of his friends to lunch.

Meals On Wheels

Barrie Bear was ill in bed, so Auntie Bear decided to take something to eat round to his house. But when everything was ready the car would not start.

'Bother!' said Auntie Bear. 'I'll have to carry the food there instead.' Then she had a clever idea . . .

Auntie Bear put all the dishes on to a trolley and she began to push it along the lane. All the time she kept a sharp lookout for anything coming up behind her.

When she came to the crossroads the policebear held up the traffic for her.

Barrie was delighted with his surprise meal. And when he was better, he bought Auntie Bear a hooter for her trolley.

THE CRAFTY COOK

Pierre Bear, the famous chef, held a cookery class one day. 'I'm going to ask you a question,' he said to his pupils. 'Anyone who gets the answer wrong will have to wash the dishes at the end of the class. The question is...how do you make a milkshake?'

The first young bear didn't know. He could only make chocolate buns.

The second young bear didn't know. He could only make strawberry jelly.

The third young bear didn't know. He could only make gingerbread bears.

But the fourth young bear put his paw up, because he knew. 'The way to make a milkshake,' he said, 'is to creep up behind it and shout BOO!' And for that awful joke Pierre Bear awarded the fourth young bear the prize of . . . washing the dishes!

THE TREASURE HUNT

One day three teddy bears found an old map, with a large black X marked on it. They couldn't read the words on the map, but they decided that it said: 'Treasure hidden here.' They guessed that the X marked where a pile of gold and silver was buried.

So the bears decided to go on a treasure hunt. They thought it might be a very long journey, so they took some supplies to keep them going — a bottle of orange juice, a box of sandwiches and several jars of honey.

This was just as well, because the words on the map actually said: 'Good picnic site'. When the bears reached the place marked on the map, they searched high and low, but they didn't find treasure hidden anywhere. So they had a delicious picnic instead, and took home only a pile of empty honey jars.

THE MAGIC EGGS

T he Wise Old Bear of the Woods was sitting dozing by the side of a footpath. Next to her was a basket of eggs. Along came Sam and Jenny all set for mischief.

'Look,' whispered Sam. 'Let's play a game with these eggs.'

'Oh, come away,' said Jenny. 'They might be magic eggs, and the old bear might put a spell on you.'

Sam just laughed and quietly took the eggs from the basket. Still the Wise Old Bear slept on. Sam and Jenny began to play a game with the eggs, rolling one along the ground and trying to hit the others with it.

Soon the Wise Old Bear woke up. She opened one eye and looked at the two bears playing with the eggs. She said nothing, but smiled slyly to herself.

'Listen,' said Jenny after a minute. 'What's that?'

Sam listened. He heard a 'cheep cheep' noise coming from inside each egg. Then he heard a pecking and a cracking and the eggs started to open. Out of them hatched yellow chicks which ran all over the place.

Up jumped the Wise Old Bear.

'What have you done to my eggs?' she cried. 'Catch those chicks at once!'

It took Sam and Jenny a long time to catch all the chicks, and then they said they were sorry for being so naughty. Afterwards they often wondered if the Wise Old Bear had known that the chicks would hatch just then, or if her eggs really were magic.

BEDTIME BEARS

When a bear can hear rain
On the window pane
And the night wind moans and wails,
Any sensible Ted
Will trot off to bed
With some books of fairy tales.

The New Year Sweater

Bimbo wanted to knit Biffy a warm sweater. He wanted it to say 'Happy New Year', as Biffy would be wearing the sweater during the cold month of January.

When the time came to wind the wool, Biffy helped Bimbo. There seemed to be rather a lot of wool.

'Do you really need all this?' asked Biffy.

'Oh yes,' said Bimbo, 'I'll make it big, in case it shrinks in the wash.'

On the cold winter evenings the friends sat happily together by the fire, talking about old times while Bimbo's needles clicked. Biffy often looked at the sweater, which was growing longer and longer. 'I'm sure it's going to be too big,' he thought.

On New Year's morning Bimbo gave Biffy the parcel. Biffy opened it as though he had never seen the sweater before. It was ENORMOUS!

'Put it on,' said Bimbo excitedly. Biffy pulled it over his head and stood there with a bright smile on his face.

'It's great, Bimbo,' he said.

Bimbo looked very anxious. 'Are you sure? It looks a bit big,' he said.

'Oh no,' said Biffy. 'It's fine. I expect I'll grow into it.'

He tried hard to look as though it fitted him, but the sleeves dangled over his paws and the sweater was nearly long enough to trip him up.

Biffy looked at his friend for a minute and then began to laugh. He laughed and laughed until he was almost crying.

'Oh dear,' said Bimbo, wiping his eyes. 'You were only saying it fitted to please me, weren't you?'

'Well, yes,' admitted Biffy.

'You can't wear it like that,' laughed Bimbo. 'But I've got an idea. I'll sew some buttons along the bottom and you can use it as a sleeping bag on these cold winter nights!'

THE TOUGHEST COWBOY IN THE WORLD

The world's toughest cowboy sat in the rocking chair eating his hash. He was thinking about all the wonderful things he had done that day. He thought of the cattle he had rounded up and the rustlers he had caught. He thought of the outlaws he had chased across the prairies.

He was just thinking about the oil he had struck on his land when his mother came in with his second helping of hash.

'Ted!' she cried. 'Get out of your father's chair at once. And take your hat off in the house *and* get your feet off the stove. Whatever were you thinking about?'

'Nothing, Ma,' said the toughest cowboy in the world. 'I was just pretending.'

A Skating Surprise

Brian Bear went to his local ice rink to learn how to skate. He stepped carefully on to the ice, where lots of other bears were already gliding around gracefully in time to music.

But Brian couldn't glide at all. In fact, he couldn't stop himself slipping and sliding. He waved his paws in the air and kept wobbling backwards instead of moving forwards.

When Brian finally managed to reach the other side of the rink he was very surprised to find that all the other bears were watching him and clapping. Then the ice rink manager came over and awarded him a silver cup, which had 'Best disco ice dancer' written on it.

After his big triumph Brian gave a TV interview. He said that he had decided to give up ice-skating to give other bear skaters a chance.

'A chance to win the cup?' said the interviewer.

'No, a chance to get around safely!' said Brian, giving the cameras a big wink.

KEEP-FIT BEARS

Jake Bear and his sister, Jessie, were out walking when they saw a big sign. 'Bears' Running Race —tomorrow afternoon', it read.

'I could win that!' boasted Jake.

'So could I!' insisted Jessie.

So, next morning, they decided to do some exercises to get fit.

'I can do push-ups,' bragged Jake, lying on the ground and pushing himself up by his arms.

'So can I!' said his sister, copying him. 'I can skip for ages, too!' she added.

'Easy!' grinned Jake, borrowing her skipping-rope.

It was very hot. Soon, they both felt tired, and sat down in the shade of a tree…

'Wake up!' said Jake, some time later.

'What's wrong?' asked Jessie.

'Neither of us can win the race now,' said Jake. 'We've both slept right through it!'

STORY BEAR

No matter how I really try,
I can't think what to write.
I put my pen to paper,
And think with all my might!
It really is the silliest thing,
The words are in my head!
But when I go to write them down,
Somehow, I find they've fled!

Jake Goes Fishing

W hat are you doing?' asked Jessie.
'What does it look as though I'm doing?' said
Jake. 'I'm fishing.'

'You're not very good at it are you?' she said.

This was true. Jake kept catching his hook on his
jacket and slipping down in the water. He was so bad
that the fish kept poking their heads up and laughing at
him.

At last, one came too near and Jake caught it in his
net. It wriggled and squirmed about and he couldn't
hold it.

'Help me,' he said, holding out the net to Jessie. She
took hold of the fish in her paws. It stopped wriggling
and looked at them with sad, fishy eyes.

'I don't think he likes being out of
the water,' said Jessie.

'I don't think he does either,' said
Jake. 'Let's put him back.'

So they did, and after that the
fish sometimes let themselves get
caught in the net, just for fun,
because they knew that Jake
would always let them go again.

THE APPLE TREE

Not very many people know,
That bears love trees, but it is so!
That's why I'm planting one for me,
My very own, *my* apple tree!
Next time, when you are passing by,
Perhaps you'll stop — perhaps you'll cry,
'Look at that tree — Bear's very own!
Can you see how much it's grown?'

BASIL'S BATON

Basil went to watch an orchestra play. The conductor waved a stick.

'It's called a *baton*,' explained his dad.

'What an odd word,' thought Basil.

Later, at home, he put on a record and held up a piece of wood. As the music boomed, Basil waved his home-made baton about, swinging his arms wildly, just like the real conductor had done.

Next moment, there was a crash. Basil had knocked a plant-pot on to the floor.

'Oh, no! I hit it with my baton,' he groaned. 'It should be called my *bat*!'

CHILLY COOK

Yan is an eskimo bear, who lives far away on an iceberg near the North Pole. It is one of the coldest parts of the world, but Yan doesn't mind the cold — he loves it!

All eskimo bears have one problem. They live in igloos made of ice, which makes cooking very difficult indeed. If you live in an ice room, you can't bake a cake, fry an egg or even make a simple slice of toast without melting part of your house!

Yan thought long and hard about this problem, because his hobby is cooking. And, at last, he came up with a great idea. Now he can make his favourite food every day, but he still doesn't bake cakes, fry eggs or make toast. Instead he has become the best ice-cream cook in the world!

THE BED-BOAT!

A …a…atchoo!' sneezed Little Brown Bear.
'Oh, no!' he groaned, wiping his nose. 'I've caught a cold.'

'You must go to bed then,' said his mother.

Little Brown Bear sighed. 'Staying in bed is boring!'

But, later, as he lay there he thought of a good game. He imagined his bed was a boat, and the rest of the room was open sea.

'A storm is blowing,' thought Little Brown Bear, 'and my boat is tossing to and fro!'

He bounced and rocked about so much that he fell out of bed with a thud!

The noise brought his mother.

'What a mess you've made!' she scolded as Little Brown Bear sat on the floor with the sheets all around him.

'You had better come downstairs and sit quietly by the fire,' frowned Mum.

'Pity!' thought Little Brown Bear with a grin. 'I'd rather stay in bed, after all!'

BATHTIME BEAR

Young Bertram Bear hated Mondays,
He didn't think they were fun-days.
His mother really had to laugh,
'And all because you hate to bath!'

'You surely are a silly bear,
Look in the mirror, over there,
Your fur is in a dreadful mess,
After a bath, you'll look your best!'

So Bertram looked and sure enough,
His fur was full of leaves and stuff,
'All right,' he said, 'if you think so,
I'll scrub myself from top to toe!'

His mother was amazed at him,
For he had soap from toes to chin.
He had to say, when dry and clean,
He was the smartest bear he'd seen.

FORGETFUL TED

I've made quite sure the oven's hot
And measured out the honey,
I've warmed it in a little pot
To make it nice and runny.
But I am a forgetful Ted
And all this care I'm taking,
Has sent the thought clean from my head —
I can't think *what* I'm making.

GRANNY BEAR'S RIDE HOME

Bimbo and Biffy were collecting wood for a bonfire, but all they had on their little cart was an old armchair.

'That's not much use,' said Bimbo.

Just then they saw old Granny Bear with her shopping. She looked very tired.

'Can we carry your shopping?' asked Biffy politely.

'You can carry *me* if you like,' said old Granny Bear and climbed into the chair! The bears pulled her home, and when they arrived she gave them a bundle of firewood out of the shed for their bonfire.

'That old chair came in useful, after all,' said Bimbo.

THE BALL OF WOOL

Lucy Bear was sad. No other little bears lived near her house, so she had no one to play with. She felt lonely.

She looked around for something to do — and saw a long piece of red wool on the ground. She picked it up. 'I wonder where it leads to?' she said, and decided to find out.

Lucy followed the red wool as it zig-zagged through the long grass and across the path. Then she followed it round the big tree and under the bushes.

Lucy was so busy following the red wool that she almost bumped into a little bear standing by a gate.

'You found my wool,' said the bear. 'It rolled away when I was unpacking. I'm Ben, and I've just come to live here.'

'Oh, good,' said Lucy. 'Now I'll have a friend to play with.'

'And so will I,' said Ben.

A Fur-coloured Door

Jessie and Jake were painting their front door. They had decided to paint it the same colour as their fur, so that it wouldn't show if they splashed themselves. But they had no brown paint.

'What colours have we got?' asked Jessie.

'Red, yellow and blue,' said Jake.

'Well, mix them together,' said Jessie.

Jake set to work. He painted part of the door red, part yellow and part blue. When Jessie saw it, she laughed.

'You silly bear,' she said. 'I meant, mix them in the pot.'

Jake felt very foolish. He mixed some red and yellow and blue paint in a spare pot, and the three colours together made brown.

After they had stirred the paint well, Jessie and Jake painted the door and by the end of the day it was a lovely fur colour.

'*And* you can't see where we have splashed ourselves,' said Jake happily.

WINDY DAY

It was a windy day.

'Good,' thought Big Bear. 'I'll wash my track suit. The wind will dry it nicely.'

But the washing-machine was too hot and the track suit shrank.

'I'll never get into *that*,' thought Big. 'Still, I may as well hang it out to dry.'

That afternoon Big was fetching his track suit off the line when he saw Small Bear. Small's fur was muddy and his clothes were wet.

'What happened?' called Big.

'The wind blew me into the pond!' said Small, miserably, 'and I haven't got any dry clothes.'

'I've got just the outfit for you,' laughed Big. And he gave Small his tiny track suit!

BUNS

Sally Bear just loves to cook,
And sometimes she may let you look.
Today, of course, it's little buns,
You know — the very fruity ones.
They are delicious, can you see?
She's made them specially for me.
Perhaps there will be one for you,
I bet you'd like to taste them, too!

THE WALKING-STICK

G rrr,' growled old Brian Bear into his muffler as he watched the young bears skating. 'No one wants a useless old grizzly bear like me.'

Leaning on his walking-stick, he shuffled once round the pond and was just about to head for his lonely cottage when he heard a shout. Simon Bear had fallen through a hole in the ice!

'Please help, someone,' Simon cried. But none of the other bears dared. The ice round him was so thin, if they went too near they, too, would fall in.

'Grrrr,' growled Brian, and held out his walking-stick as far as he could. Simon grabbed hold of it and Brian pulled and pulled until at last Simon was safely clear of the icy water.

Simon's family held a party in honour of Brian.

'You saved my son's life,' said Simon's father. 'How can I ever thank you enough?'

'Grrrr,' growled Brian, but this time he was smiling.

THE RUSTY RACER

Charlie had an old motor-car called 'Rusty'. It was battered and bent, but he enjoyed driving it. One day Charlie decided to enter Rusty for a race. He spent hours under the car, twiddling and fiddling with the engine.

On the day of the race Charlie drove Rusty up to the starting line. All the other cars looked very smart and shiny. They had stripes painted along their sides, and rows of sharp teeth painted on them. They looked as if they could go very fast, and made Rusty look scruffy and slow.

The marshal began the race. 'Ready, teddy, go!' he shouted. Rusty started at the back, but even though he looked scruffy he had the best engine in the competition. He overtook the other cars one by one, and crossed the finishing line first!

When they got home, Charlie cleaned and polished Rusty. And to make him look like a real champion, he painted a number one on Rusty's door, and a big winning smile across his front.

SCARECROW TED

P ut on your clean sweater and jeans,' said Ted's mother one morning. But instead, Ted put on some old clothes and a jacket with a big tear in it.

When his mother saw him she sighed and said, 'There's an old hat in the rag bag, why don't you wear that too? You'll look just like a scarecrow.'

Ted knew she was only joking but, just to be clever, he put it on and went out. He did look a fright.

As he was passing the house next door, old Mr Grizzly called out, 'Hello, Ted, you're just the bear I've been looking for. I've planted some seeds. Will you stand in my garden and stop the birds eating them?'

Ted felt very foolish, standing all morning in Mr Grizzly's garden and, eventually, he went home and changed into his clean sweater and jeans.

'What have you been doing all morning?' asked his mother.

'Scaring the crows!' said Ted.

A Present from the Three Bears

We've bought some lovely presents:
A clock that ticks and tocks,
A silver star,
A special pair,
Of multi-coloured socks,

I've put them with a message
Inside this little box:
'From Ma and Pa
And Baby Bear
To our friend, Goldilocks.'

Ted and the Violin

Ted took his violin into the park to practise. He took off his hat and began to play. He wasn't very good. In fact, he made an awful noise.

Scratch, screech, wail.

After a while some bears came up, and threw some money into his hat which had fallen off the bench.

'I'm glad you like my playing,' said Ted, and continued, louder than before.

Scratch, screech, wail.

'We're not paying you because we like your playing,' said one big bear. 'We're paying you to go to take some lessons!'

JIM'S BABY BROTHER

I've got things to do,' said Jim's mother. 'Can you keep Baby Bear happy for a while?'

'Of course I can,' said Jim. 'That's easy, really easy.'

'Thank you,' said his mother.

'Hello, Baby Bear,' Jim said in a high squeaky voice. Baby smiled for a while, then started to cry.

Jim put his paws over his eyes and played hide-and-peep. Baby looked, smiled once, then started to cry.

Jim put his arms up by his head and pointed his paws. 'Look, I'm a rabbit,' he said. Baby cried.

Jim pulled funny faces till his jaw ached. Baby smiled, then started to cry.

Jim tickled Baby under his chin. Baby cried.

Jim was fed up. This wasn't as easy as it looked. He went to find his mother.

'Er, could you keep Baby Bear happy for a while?' asked Jim. 'I've got things to do.'

And before his mother could answer, Jim was gone.

EXERCISES

A nnabel Bear wanted to lose weight and get fit. So, early one morning she went to a special bears' exercise class.

She started her class by lifting some weights to exercise her paws. Then she lay on her back and pedalled in the air to exercise her legs. Finally she touched her toes to exercise her tummy.

Annabel was allowed to eat only three lettuce leaves for lunch, and then she started all over again. She jumped up and down to exercise

her ankles and swung to and fro to exercise her waist. Then she jogged around the room to exercise everything else. By the end of the day Annabel was *very* tired.

The next morning Annabel didn't turn up to her class at all. She stayed at home in bed and exercised her eyes by keeping them tightly closed. This is Annabel's favourite exercise — it's called sleeping!

TINY TED'S SHADOW

Tiny Ted couldn't find it. Where *had* it gone? It had been there a few minutes ago. He twisted and turned and looked over his shoulder but no, it wasn't there.

'What are you looking for?' called big sister Binkie.

'My shadow,' said Tiny Ted. 'I had it before I came to stand under this tree.'

'Come out into the sunshine,' laughed Binkie.

Tiny Ted ran out of the shade of the tree, and there was his shadow again.

'There it is,' said Tiny Ted. 'I thought I had lost it.'

'You silly bear,' said Binkie. 'The sun makes your shadow, so you can't lose it.'

Tiny Ted was so pleased he did a little dance and his shadow did a little dance too.

A Clever Place To Hide

When they played hide-and-seek at Biffy's Christmas party, Tiny Ted hid so well, no one could find him. They still hadn't found him when it was time to give out the prizes from the tree.

'Tiny Ted's won the prize for hide-and-seek,' said Biffy, 'but where is he?'

'I'm here,' piped up a voice, and there was Tiny Ted *on* the Christmas tree. He had climbed up and fastened himself on to look like one of the prizes.

'Well,' said Biffy, 'who would have thought of looking *there*.'

Outer-space Ted

I'm going to Mars in my space ship —
I'm off for a year and a day.
I'm all kitted out in the right kind of gear
And the seconds are ticking away.

It's all-systems-go on the launch pad,
I'll be out in space double-quick.
I am the best astrobear in the world
But I do wish I didn't feel sick!

RAG AND BONE BEAR AND THE SOFA

Rag and Bone Bear hadn't picked up much old furniture or junk that day. He only had an old sofa on his cart.

'That's not much use,' he thought.

Just then, he passed a bus-stop and saw Mrs Next-door Bear waiting.

'Are you all right?' he called.

'No, I'm not, since you ask,' said Mrs Next-door Bear. 'My back aches and my feet are killing me and I'm dying for a nice cold drink.'

'Let me give you a ride on my cart.'

Up got Mrs Next-door Bear and sat on the sofa. Her back stopped aching and her feet stopped hurting, and when they got home she gave Rag and Bone Bear a large glass of orange juice.

'That old sofa came in useful after all,' said Rag and Bone Bear.

ODD SOCKS

The twins, Bobby and Beth, were watching their mother put clean clothes into their chest of drawers. When she had finished, there were four socks left. Four odd socks — a black sock, a white sock, a grey sock and a brown sock. 'I can't find any socks to match these,' she said. 'Throw them away will you, Bobby? Odd socks are just no use at all.'

'I know what we can do with odd socks,' said Beth, and she whispered in Bobby's ear.

'That's a great idea,' said Bobby. 'Let's get started.'

Bobby and Beth took some felt and cut out different shapes — ears, noses, eyes and mouths. They glued them on to the odd socks and, before long, the black sock was a cat, the white sock was a mouse, the grey sock was a rabbit and the brown sock was a dog.

Bobby and Beth put their hands inside the odd socks. 'Look,' they said to their mother. 'We've made some sock puppets to play with!'

There is a use for odd socks!

AUNT MIMI'S GIFT

A big brown envelope dropped through the door of Jamie and Kate's house. In it was a letter from their Aunt Mimi and four packets of seeds. 'Plant the seeds outside,' Jamie read, 'and when the flowers have grown I'll come and visit.'

Jamie and Kate had their own patches of ground outside where no one else was allowed to grow things. They took their seed packets — one white and one blue each — and started to plant them.

'I'm going to make a pattern with my seeds,' said Kate. 'A secret pattern.'

'I'm going to make a pattern too,' said Jamie. 'And I'm not going to tell you what it is. You'll have to wait and see.'

Jamie and Kate knelt down back to back and carefully smoothed out the soil. Then they started to sprinkle the seeds over the soil — first the white packet, then the blue. When all the seeds were used up, they covered them with a thin layer of earth and watered them.

'Now all we have to do is wait,' said Kate.

Every day Jamie and Kate went outside to look at their seed beds. They watered the soil if it was dry.

Soon, tiny green shoots started to push their way up through the soil.

Day by day the shoots grew, then small green leaves appeared. Every day the tiny plants grew stronger, with more and more leaves.

As the weeks passed the plants grew taller and taller, and quite soon small flower buds appeared at the top of each plant. The buds grew fatter and fatter until they looked as if they would burst open.

When Aunt Mimi arrived Jamie took one of her paws and Kate the other. 'The flowers opened this morning,' said Kate.

'Come and look,' said Jamie, and they led Aunt Mimi to the back of the house.

In the flower beds were two patterns, both in blue flowers on a white background. 'How lovely,' said Aunt Mimi. 'A blue J for Jamie and a blue K for Kate!'

DECORATING

I'm going to the shops to buy some paint,' said Dad. 'We're going to decorate this room.'

'What shall we do?' said Kate when Dad had gone.

'Let's do the decorating,' said Jamie. 'Dad will be pleased.'

Jamie mixed paste in a big bucket and Kate found a roll of wallpaper. She cut a long piece and Jamie slapped on lots of paste. Soon there was more paste on Kate's fur than on the wallpaper.

Kate put the paper on the wall. Instead of a smooth strip it went on in a crinkly lump.

'Maybe it will be better when it dries,' said Jamie, and stepped back. SPLOOOSH! His foot went into the bucket of paste!

Just then Dad came back. 'Look at this mess!' he said angrily. Then he saw Kate's sticky fur and Jamie's pasted foot and started to laugh. 'Now we really will have to decorate — and without any *help* from you two!'

SNOW BEAR

B ertram Bear looked out one day,
He noticed it was snowing,
'Whoopee!' he shouted loudly,
'I know where I am going!'
He ran into his garden,
You should have seen folk stare,
For pretty soon you couldn't see,
What was snow and what was bear!

THE MUDDY BOOTS

W ipe your boots!' said Mrs Bear as Little Brown Bear walked in, leaving muddy marks on the kitchen floor. His mother wiped them up.

'*You* can clean your boots,' she said. 'What a mess they're in!'

Mrs Bear went into the garden to hang up some washing. Little Brown Bear had an idea. He put his boots into the washing-machine.

When Mrs Bear saw them spinning about, she was cross and pulled them out.

'They're all wet and soapy!' she scolded. 'Why did you do that?'

'To clean them. There's not a bit of mud on my boots now!' said Little Brown Bear.

THE BUTTERFLY HAT

Ted put a net on the end of a stick and went into the wood to try to catch some butterflies.

The butterflies did not like this one bit and fluttered around trying to keep out of his way.

Big Bertha came for a walk in the wood. She was wearing a new hat with a big red bow on the top. She sat down on a grassy bank where Ted could not see her. All he could see was the bow on her hat.

'What a beautiful butterfly,' thought Ted.

Up he crept and, whoosh, down came his net on Big Bertha's hat.

Up jumped Bertha in an awful rage and began to chase Ted out of the wood.

Ted ran home and hid behind the door. 'Being chased isn't much fun,' he thought, and after that, he left the poor little butterflies alone.

THE WORST VOICE IN THE WORLD

The twins thought their grandad had a terrible voice. One day he told them he had entered a singing competition.

'Don't do it, Grandad,' begged the twins, but he laughed and said he was sure to win.

When the evening came, the twins sat right at the back of the hall. Some of the singers weren't very good but when it came to Grandad, the bears in the audience laughed and stamped their paws and the twins' fur turned quite pink with embarrassment.

To their amazement, at the end of the show they heard that Grandad had won first prize. It was a big box of nuts.

What Grandad hadn't told them was that the competition was to find the bear with the *worst* voice in the world.

'I told you I would win, didn't I?' laughed Grandad as he shared his prize with the twins.

THE BIRD-BEAR

I can fly!' said Roger Bear, as his friend Billy Bear arrived.

'Bet you can't!' said Billy. 'You're not a bird.'

'I'm the first bird-bear!' replied Roger. 'Watch!'

He had made two big paper wings and tied them to his arms.

'Stand by for take-off!' Roger shouted. But instead of flying, he dived straight down and almost landed on Billy.

'Never mind,' said Billy. 'Let's go camping instead.'

So the bears went to collect their camping gear.

'I'll put the tent up,' said Roger, later. But as Roger held the tent, a big gust of wind suddenly filled it like a balloon. It flew into the air and so did Roger! But he soon came to earth with a bump.

'You flew just now!' said Billy, when Roger landed.

'I don't think bears are made for flying after all!' gasped Roger.

BABY HONEY BEAR

H ave you seen Baby Honey Bear?
I have searched for him here and there,
He isn't in his cot, I'm sure,
Perhaps he is behind the door?
When I peer round, he says 'Boo'
Now that's a thing he likes to do!
But, no, he isn't there — instead,
He's hiding underneath the bed!

AUNTIE SUE'S SWEATER

I 've knitted you a sweater,' said Auntie Sue to young Brown Bear. 'Try it on.' So he did. But it was much too big.

Just then, his sister came into the room.

'I love that sweater!' she said.

'Try it on,' smiled Auntie Sue.

So she did. But it stretched down to her knees.

'It's too big for you, too,' grinned young Brown Bear.

'No, it isn't,' replied his sister, putting on a belt. 'See? I'll wear it as a *dress*!'

BRUNO'S SPECIAL DAY

It was a special day for Bruno, and he wanted to share it with his friends.

He found his friend Sam. 'Shall we play cowboys?' asked Bruno.

'Can't,' said Sam. 'I'm busy today,' and he rushed off.

Bruno met Sally. 'Shall we play?' said Bruno. 'It's my...'

Before Bruno could finish, Sally shook her head. 'I'm busy,' she said. 'Bye.'

Bruno saw his friend, Ella, with a parcel. 'Where are you going?' he asked.

'I can't tell you,' said Ella. 'It's a secret.'

Bruno felt sad. None of his friends wanted to play with him. They were all going somewhere, and wouldn't tell him *where*. And on today of all days.

Bruno went home. As he opened the door he saw Sam, Sally and Ella. 'Surprise!' they shouted. 'Happy birthday, Bruno!'

'So this is where you were going,' said Bruno.

'Yes, to your birthday party!' said Sam.

BASIL'S GARDEN

Basil Bear watched his dad doing the gardening. 'What beautiful flowers,' he said.

'They're prize-winners,' replied Basil's dad. He was very proud of his garden.

'I'd like a garden, too,' said Basil.

'You can have a patch of mine,' his dad grinned. So he cut a new flower-bed in the lawn.

Then Basil worked, digging and raking it, until his back ached. Next morning, he planted some seeds. They grew into a neat row of bright flowers which stood up like soldiers.

'Look, Dad!' called Basil, excitedly. But it was a hot day and the flowers soon drooped.

'Gardens must be watered,' said his dad.

After a while, Basil was busy doing other things and forgot o tend his garden. But it kept on growing.

'You grow the best flowers around,' he told his dad a few weeks later. Then Basil glanced at his own overgrown garden. 'And I grow the best *weeds*!'

BUNTY HEARS THE SEA

Barbara went on holiday to the seaside, and while she was away she sent a lovely picture postcard to Betty. It was a view of the beach. The sea was deep blue and the waves coming on to the shore were tipped with white.

'Thank you for your picture,' said Betty when Barbara came back. 'I've never seen the sea.'

'I know,' said Barbara, 'but I've brought you a present so that you can *hear* it.'

She brought a large shell out of her bag. Betty looked surprised but, when she put it to her ear, she really thought she could hear the sea roaring, deep down inside the shell.

THE DAISY CHAINS

Barbara and Brenda were walking through a field when they saw Bertie asleep among the daisies.

'Wake up, Bertie,' they called.

'I'm not asleep,' said Bertie. 'I'm thinking.'

When the bears went past later, they saw him fast asleep again. They sat down beside him and began to make daisy chains. Soon they called, 'Wake up Bertie.'

Bertie pretended again that he hadn't been asleep at all.

'I was thinking,' he said.

'Well, look what we've done while you were deep in thought,' they said.

Bertie tried to stand up and look around, but to his surprise he couldn't; the other bears had tied him up — with daisy chains!

A LONG COUNTRY WALK

W ait for me!' called Tiny Ted.
Binkie and Bertie looked round and saw their
very small brother hurrying after them. They were
setting off for a long country walk and had bags on
their backs to carry their food and waterproof clothes.

'You can't come, Tiny Ted,' said Bertie. 'You'll get
tired.'

'I won't,' said Tiny Ted. 'Look, I've got my boots
and a packed lunch. Please let me come. I'll be a good
bear.'

'No,' said Bertie, and Tiny
Ted sat down on the floor and
began to cry.

Binkie was very miserable.
She wanted Tiny Ted to come too, but
he only had very short legs and couldn't
have kept up. Then she had an idea.
She whispered to
Bertie and he
began taking
things out of his
bag and putting them into
Binkie's. And guess what went
into Bertie's bag? Tiny Ted!

'Hurray,' he called. 'I'm
going for a long country
walk, after all.'

WISE OLD BEAR LOSES HIS
SPECTACLES

Wise Old Bear called to see the young bears' mother and while he was there, he lost his spectacles.

Mrs Bear was in the kitchen making a drink, so Wise Old Bear asked Binkie to look for his lost spectacles.

'I've put them down somewhere,' he said.

Binkie was too shy to tell him where they were.

In came Bertie with some nuts in a bowl.

'Have you seen my spectacles?' asked Wise Old Bear.

Bertie didn't like to tell him where they were in case it sounded impolite.

In came Mrs Bear with the drinks.

'Have you seen my spectacles?' asked Wise Old Bear.

Mrs Bear looked very flustered. She didn't want to make him look silly in front of the young bears.

In came Tiny Ted and climbed on to Wise Old Bear's knee. Then he put the spectacles back on Wise Old Bear's nose. They were sitting on his head all the time!

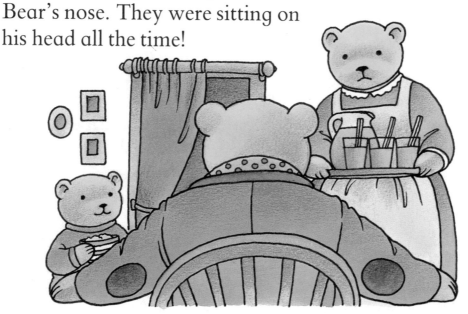

BUSTER'S BALLOON RIDE

B uster's auntie had given him an enormous balloon with a basket on the bottom so that he could go for rides up in the air. There was plenty of room for two bears, or even three, but Buster was very selfish and wouldn't let anyone else go with him.

He didn't mind asking for help though, and sometimes Binkie, Biffy and Bimbo would come to give him a good send-off.

One day, Binkie had asked him to take Tiny Ted for a little ride. Buster had said 'no', not very politely, and now Binkie and Tiny Ted were nowhere to be seen.

'Sulking, I suppose,' said Buster. The basket seemed very heavy and he threw out the bags of sand that stopped him going up in the air too quickly.

Then he was off.

Slowly, slowly, the balloon rose up in the air on the end of its long rope and, just as it reached the top of the trees, Tiny Ted and Binkie crawled out from under a rug.

Buster was furious.

'Stand by below,' he yelled. 'I've got two stowaways on board.'

Bimbo and Biffy pulled him down again by the rope, and Buster made Binkie and Tiny Ted get out. He was in such a bad temper, he forgot that the basket would now be much lighter. As soon as the stowaways were out, the balloon shot up into the air.

Bimbo and Biffy were so surprised that they let go of the rope and the balloon went flying off with Buster in the basket.

'Help! Help!' he called.

Luckily for him, the basket caught in a tree and the bears were able to rescue him.

Buster was grateful and he realized that he had been very selfish.

'You can all come for balloon rides tomorrow,' said Buster, 'and Tiny Ted can be first.'

'Thank you, Buster,' said an excited Tiny Ted.

HONEY SPOTS

Little Brown Bear stood before the mirror and brushed his fur. Just then, a bee landed on the window.

'I wish *I* had nice, bright yellow stripes,' thought Little Brown Bear. Later, in the kitchen, he saw a large pot of honey.

'Mm! Delicious!' he said, picking up the pot and scooping out a pawful. Suddenly, the pot slipped and honey splashed everywhere.

'Oh, no!' groaned Little Brown Bear. Soon, his mother scolded him and sent him to wash.

'Why,' grinned Little Brown Bear as he looked in the mirror, 'now I'm brown with delicious golden *spots* all over me!'

HURLY BURLY BEAR

My name is Hurly Burly Bear,
I rush and tear just everywhere.
I really cannot stop and chat,
There is no time for doing that.
I have so much to do, you see,
And no one does it quite like me!

THE BROWN BEARS' BARBECUE

T eddy Bears *always* have picnics!' said young Brown Bear. 'Let's do something different.'

'Like have a barbecue,' his sister said.

'Good idea!' agreed Mr Brown.

'It's not,' said Mrs Brown. 'I've already made sandwiches for a picnic.' But the other Brown Bears insisted on a barbecue.

'I'll grill tomatoes, steaks, bacon and burgers,' said Mr Brown, lighting the barbecue. But the smoke got in his eyes. It made them water.

It made young Brown Bear cough.

It made his sister cough.

It made Mrs Brown cross, especially when Mr Brown burnt the food black.

'The flames were too fierce. We've nothing to eat,' moaned the bears. 'What shall we do?'

'Have a picnic,' said Mrs Brown, 'like bears should. I brought the sandwiches along, just in case.'

CONTRARY TED

Tiny Ted was feeling bored.

Binkie was doing her homework and had no time to play with him.

'Go out in the garden,' she said.

But he wouldn't go in the garden.

'Don't tease the cat,' she said.

So Tiny Ted pulled pussy's tail.

Whatever Binkie told Tiny Ted to do he did just the opposite.

At last, Binkie, who now knew Tiny Ted's little ways, said, 'I don't care what you do as long as you don't play with my building bricks.'

Immediately, Tiny Ted got out the building bricks. He played happily with them all morning and Binkie did her homework in peace.

STRONG-ARM BIFFY

Biffy was showing all the other bears how strong he was. He had some very heavy weights and he lifted them up slowly and held them above his head for a minute.

'Do be careful,' called Binkie. 'You'll hurt yourself.'

'I won't,' said Biffy, and lifted an even bigger one.

This time it looked really difficult, but at last he managed to lift the weights right above his head! The other bears clapped and said he must be the strongest bear in the world.

Biffy bowed to the applause with a big grin on his face and then winked at Tiny Ted. Tiny Ted jumped off Binkie's knee and said, 'It's my turn now.'

Before Binkie could stop him he had run to the biggest weight and picked it up in one hand.

Biffy had only been pretending. The weights were made of plastic and were as light as feathers!

RAINBOW BEAR

S usie Teddy liked having her fur styled in all kinds of different ways. She could never decide which style looked best. She tried having a big red bow on top of her head. She tried making her fur curly, then fluffy, then spiky. Susie must have tried every teddy bear fashion there was.

One day Susie went to the beauty salon and had her fur washed and left straight, short and neat. But when she went home no one recognized her! Susie looked just like every other bear, and her friends had never seen her like that before!

So the next day Susie went back to the beauty salon and had her fur dyed in many different colours. After that, no one had any trouble recognizing her. Susie didn't look like any other bear — she looked more like a walking rainbow!

THE INVISIBLE MOUSE

Everywhere Tom went he was followed by a squeaky sound. He decided that it was a mouse. When he went up the stairs the squeaky mouse went too. And if he played outside the squeaky mouse always joined in.

No matter how hard he tried, Tom never saw the mouse.

Sometimes he would walk along pretending not to notice the squeak. Then he would turn around quickly to surprise it. But when he did that, the squeak always disappeared straight away.

Sometimes Tom would try to chase the squeaky mouse. But it just squeaked faster and faster, and Tom could never catch it.

The noise went away the day Tom bought some new boots and put his old shoes away in a cupboard. A few days later he realized that his friendly squeaky mouse had disappeared. It was his old shoes that had squeaked all the time, not a mouse at all!

ROGER THE PIRATE

R oger Bear loved playing pirates. He hoisted a pirate flag on the mast of his home-made raft, then set sail on the pond. Roger wore a pirate hat, cut from paper, and a cardboard cutlass in his belt. His mother had sewed him a black eye-patch.

'Avast, me hearty!' he shouted fiercely, like a real pirate. He had seen Billy Bear beside the pond.

'I'm Black Patch the pirate!' said Roger.

Billy joined in the game. 'I'm Jolly Jake, terror of the high seas,' he shouted.

'Attack!' roared Roger, bringing his boat closer. But he slipped and fell into thick, sticky mud.

'I can see why they call you Black Patch,' grinned Billy, pulling him out by his paws. 'You've got mud all over you!'

GROWL!

There was once a young bear who could not growl. He would huff, strain and puff. But the noise he made was more like 'squeak'!

'Oh, dear!' sighed the bear. 'That doesn't sound fierce, at all!'

So he went to see his dad.

'Open your mouth wider, and take a very deep breath,' said Dad. 'It's easy, really.'

All day long, the young bear tried his hardest.

'GROWWWWWWWL!' he went, at last.

'That did sound fierce!' grinned Dad.

'I know,' said the young bear, shivering. 'It even frightened *me*!'

VANITY BEAR

I think that I will never see,
A bear as beautiful as me!
Look at my ears so long and brown,
My fur is fine as thistle down.
My eyes are clear and starry-bright,
And when I roar into the night,
My voice is just the best around,
A finer bear cannot be found!

THE PICTURE WINDOW

When Becky Bear peered out of her bedroom window one cold morning, she couldn't see a thing! 'How odd!' she thought. 'Where has the world gone?'

Becky touched the window-pane. It was covered in frost.

'How silly of me,' she smiled. 'The window's frosted.'

'You can't go out today,' said Becky's mother, bringing in breakfast on a tray, 'you've not been well.'

'I'll do some drawing then,' said Becky. But she could not find any paper.

'I'm going shopping,' said her mother. 'I'll buy you some.'

When she came back, she handed Becky a big sketchbook.

'There,' she said. 'What have you been up to?'

'I've been drawing,' replied Becky, with a smile.

Her mother was surprised. 'But you said you had no paper,' she said.

'I didn't need any,' Becky said, pulling back the curtains. 'See? I drew a picture with my paw on the frosty window!'

ROOTIN' TOOTIN' BEAR

I'm a rootin', tootin' cowboy — from the Wild West!' boomed the bear, dressed in his ten-gallon hat, leather boots and shining spurs.

Actually, his name was Stanley and he came from Honeypot Cottage. But he did like to pretend…

'Yes, siree. Just call me "Slim"!' said Stanley, as he saw Susie Bear about to hang out her washing.

So Slim…er, Stanley… whirled a rope above his head.

'This is called a lasso, Miss Susie. Watch me spin it.'

But the rope slipped and fell over him. How Susie laughed.

Suddenly, her washing-line snapped.

'Oh, dear! I'll never get my washing dry now, unless…'

Susie had an idea. She untangled the lasso from Stanley, then tied it between two trees.

'There! It makes a perfect washing-line,' she smiled. 'Thank you, Slim.'

'Glad to be of help,' said Stanley. 'Mighty glad!'

MR GRUMPS

One day Tiny Ted saw Mr Grumps building a fence round his garden.

'What's that for?' he asked.

'To keep you young bears out,' said Mr Grumps.

The next day Mr Grumps was driving along in his truck when he saw Tiny Ted and his mother at the bus stop. They waved to him and he stopped.

'Could you give us a lift to the fair?' asked Ted.

'I suppose so,' said Mr Grumps.

He looked very grumpy as they set off but Tiny Ted and his mother were smiling happily. They hadn't gone very far when Tiny Ted said, 'Look! There are Biffy and Bimbo. Can they come too?'

'I suppose so,' grumbled Mr Grumps, and in climbed Biffy and Bimbo.

They hadn't gone much further when Tiny Ted said, 'Oh, look, there are Betty and Barbara and Bertie. Can they come too?'

'I suppose so,' grumbled Mr Grumps, and in climbed Betty and Barbara and Bertie.

They hadn't gone much further when Tiny Ted said, 'Oh look, there are Bernard and Brenda and Binkie. Can they come too?'

'I suppose so,' grumbled Mr Grumps, and in climbed Bernard and Brenda and Binkie.

When they reached the fair, out climbed Tiny Ted and his mother and Biffy and Bimbo and Betty and Barbara and Bertie and Bernard and Brenda and Binkie.

They called out 'thank you' and ran off to the fair.

'Aren't you coming, too, Mr Grumps?' asked Tiny Ted.

'I suppose so,' grumbled Mr Grumps.

Mr Grumps really enjoyed himself at the fair. He even offered the bears a ride home afterwards.

The next day, Mr Grumps was at work on his fence.

'What are you doing?' asked Tiny Ted.

'I'm pulling down my fence. I'm going to burn it.'

He made a huge bonfire and asked all the bears in the neighbourhood to come to it. Tiny Ted and his mother and Biffy and Bimbo and Betty and Barbara and Bertie and Bernard and Brenda and Binkie and many other bears came along. It was great fun.

. 'Are you enjoying yourself?' asked Tiny Ted's mother.

'I suppose so,' smiled Mr Grumps.

HIDE-AND-SEEK

Jake and Tim were playing hide-and-seek. 'You hide first,' said Jake. 'I'll close my eyes, count to ten, then come and look for you.'

Tim rushed off as Jake started to count. 'One, two . . .'

When he got to ten Jake opened his eyes. Tim was gone.

Jake looked in the wardrobe, but Tim wasn't there. He looked under the bed, but all he found was a pair of shoes. Then he looked in the cupboard under the stairs, but it was empty. Next Jake looked under the table — no Tim.

Jake stood at the tall window. 'Where is that bear?' he said, and he heard a soft, snuffling, trying-not-to-giggle noise beside him. He pulled back the long curtain, and there was Tim. 'Found you!' said Jake. 'Now it's my turn to hide.'

Tim closed his eyes and started to count. Before he got to three, Jake was gone.

By now, Jake knew all the best hiding places. Can you guess where he hid?

THE TARTAN RUG

Duncan's paws trembled with disappointment. His one and only Christmas present had turned out to be not a bicycle or skates or even a book or a jigsaw, but a boring old tartan rug. It was the sort of present you'd give a grandmother bear, not a seven-year-old boy bear. And his friends would make such fun of him. They always got lots of exciting Christmas presents.

'It's a special rug,' explained his mother. 'You can turn it into anything you want.'

Duncan thought. Perhaps he could. First he turned it into a tent, then into a hammock, then into a magician's cloak. Finally he imagined it was a magic carpet on which he flew to all sorts of exciting lands. And at night it kept him beautifully warm.

'What did you get for Christmas, then, Duncan?' asked his friends.

'A tent, a hammock, a magician's cloak *and* a magic carpet,' smiled Duncan. And you should have seen his friends' faces turn green with envy!

TOAST FOR TEA

O ne evening when Bimbo and Biffy were sitting by their cosy fireside, Bimbo said, 'I would like some toast, but the toaster is broken.'

'There's more than one way to make toast,' said Biffy. He went into the kitchen and came back with some slices of bread and a long fork. He stuck the fork into a slice of bread and held it up before the fire. The warm glow from the fire turned the bread a lovely golden brown. It smelled delicious.

Biffy put the toasted bread on a plate, spread it with butter and gave it to Bimbo.

'Try that,' he said.

Bimbo bit into the hot buttered toast. It *was* delicious.

'Mmm,' he said. 'That was just what I wanted. How clever you are, Biffy. Now, is there anything I can do for you?'

'How about washing the dishes!' said Biffy as he made some toast for himself.

BERNARD'S BOW-TIE

Bernard wanted to tie his neck-tie in a bow like Bertie's, but Bertie wouldn't show him how it was done. First, Bernard tried himself, but it came out

wrong Then Brenda tried, but it was too loose. Biffy tried, and hit him on the chin by mistake. Brian tried, and nearly choked him.

Then Bertie realized what was wrong. He had bought a bow that was already tied, and all he had to do was clip it on to his collar!

UPSIDE-DOWN TED

Upside-down Ted
Likes to stand on his head
Especially just before tea.

An upside-down bear
With his feet in the air
Is a thing you don't often see.

My mum thinks I'm mad
And so does my dad
Because upside-down Teddy is me!

THE CLEVER CATCH

S tanley Bear sat by the river, fishing. Susie Bear
came along, to show him her new hat.

'Watch me catch something for my supper,' said
Stanley. Next moment, his fishing-line strained.

'It must be a big fish!' puffed Stanley, pulling hard.

'It's a big, old boot!' laughed Susie. Stanley felt silly.
But he tried again. This time, he hooked out a rusty
saucepan.

Just then, Susie's hat blew off and landed in the
water. Carefully, Stanley caught it with his fishing-line
and brought it back to the riverbank.

'Clever Stanley,' smiled Susie. 'You *have* caught
something for your supper.'

'I can't eat your hat,' replied Stanley, puzzled.

'No,' said Susie. 'But for catching it, you can have
supper with me.'

TEDDY BEARS' TALK

Once a year and only once,
  The Teddy Bears get together,
They have a sort of business lunch,
For bears are very clever!
They talk about lots of things,
Like berries and good honey,
And how to be more cuddly,
And what makes tickles funny!

HIGH-SPEED BEARS

Whoosh! Vroom! Swish!
    Roger Bear went everywhere at full speed on his skateboard. So did his friend Billy Bear.
  Zoom!
  They sped downhill and round a corner.
  'Look out!' warned Arnold Bear. He nearly dropped a big box he was carrying. 'You're pests with those skateboards!' he said, crossly. 'It's hard enough carrying this box. It's heavy!'

'We'll help you,' said Roger and Billy.
    They put the box across their skateboards and pushed it along easily.
    'Maybe skateboards aren't so bad, after all,' grinned Arnold, happily.

IMPOSSIBLE

T homas Bear was reading to his grandfather. 'This is a long word,' said Thomas, pointing to the page. 'What does it say?'

Grandfather spelt out the word. 'IMPOSSIBLE,' he said.

'Impossible,' said Thomas. 'What does it mean?'

Grandfather thought hard. 'Impossible means something that's very, very difficult,' he said. 'Something that just can't be done.'

'Oh,' said Thomas. 'Like eating ten doughnuts all at once?'

Grandfather laughed. 'Something like that,' he said, and closed the book. 'That's enough reading for today. Come outside and help me clear the dead leaves away. We'll leave your grandmother to have her afternoon snooze.'

Grandfather gave Thomas a broom. 'Sweep the leaves off the path,' he said. 'And try not to disturb your grandmother.'

Thomas swept the leaves along the path. Rustle, rustle, crinkle, crackle went the leaves.

Thomas swept the leaves into a big, golden pile. Rustle, rustle, crinkle, crackle went the leaves.

Grandfather brought the wheelbarrow, and Thomas

picked up big armfuls of dried leaves and put them inside. Rustle, rustle, crinkle, crackle went the leaves.

Grandfather wheeled the barrow to the rubbish heap and Thomas tipped out the dried leaves. Rustle, rustle, crinkle, crackle went the leaves.

'Good,' said Grandfather. 'Let's go inside and get warmed up.'

In the kitchen Grandfather and Thomas drank mugs of hot chocolate. 'I've been thinking,' said Thomas. 'I know something that's impossible.'

'What's that?' asked Grandfather.

'It's *impossible* to collect dry leaves quietly,' said Thomas. 'No matter how hard you try, it just can't be done. They go rustle, rustle, crinkle, crackle as soon as you touch them!'

THE TWINS GO CAMPING

P lease may we go camping?' asked the twins, Bobby and Beth.

'No, you're too young,' said their mother.

Bobby and Beth looked so sad that Mrs Bear thought hard. 'Why not try *pretend* camping?' she said. 'Bring the big tablecloth and the tartan rug and I'll show you how.'

Mrs Bear threw the big tablecloth over the dining-table so that it touched the floor all round, and spread the rug under the table. 'This is your tent,' she said.

Bobby and Beth crawled inside. 'This is great,' they said. 'It's just like a real tent.'

A few minutes later the twins heard their mother's voice. 'This is a special delivery for the campers,' she said. 'Apples, orange juice and chocolate cake.'

'Great!' said the twins. 'This is even *better* than real camping!'

GHOSTS

Poppy and Sue were bored. Then Poppy had an idea for some fun.

She pulled the white sheet off her bed and put it over her head. 'Look at me, I'm a ghost!' she cried.

Then Sue put a sheet over her head. 'I'm a ghost, too,' she said. 'Let's go and surprise Mother.'

Downstairs, Poppy and Sue waved their arms and made eerie ghostly noises.

'Wheee!' said Poppy.

'Whooo!' said Sue.

'Eeeek — ghosts!' screamed their mother as she ran away to hide. But she was only pretending, and she soon came back and sent Poppy and Sue back to bed with the promise of a scary Hallowe'en bedtime story.

TEDDY BEAR'S SHADOW

Have you seen Teddy Bear's shadow?
There — behind him — on the ground.
It never says a single word,
And it never makes a sound.
But his shadow's always with him,
Just following him around.

THE GET-WELL SNOWBEAR

One morning Ted woke up covered in spots. Dr Bear came and said he must stay away from his friends in case they turned spotty too.

What made things worse was that it was snowing, and his mother had made him promise not to get out of bed to look through the window. Ted could hear the other bears having such fun in the snow outside.

Feeling very sorry for himself, Ted covered up his head with the quilt and tried not to cry.

'Nobody cares,' he thought.

After a while, his mother came in and told him to put on his dressing gown.

'Keep very warm,' she said, 'and look through the window.'

What do you think Ted saw?

The garden was filled with his friends, and they had made him a big snowbear. Round its neck was a card, and on the card they had written 'Get Well Soon'.

Ted laughed and waved and thought, 'I should have known they wouldn't forget me.'

THE RUNAWAY BAND

There was great excitement in town. The President was coming on a visit and the town band was all ready to march past and play to him.

'Now everything is clear, I hope,' said Bandmaster Bear. 'When I say "Quick March" you start, and when I say "Halt" you stop.'

When the great day came and the President was standing on the platform, Bandmaster Bear called out 'Quick March'. Off went the band, flags flying, trumpets tootling and drums banging. On they marched until it was time to stop. But the bandmaster could not remember the right word.

He ran along beside them calling 'Stop, stop,' but they took no notice. On they marched until they were almost at the river.

'Stop, stop,' called everyone standing by. But still the band marched on.

Just as they came to the river bank, a resourceful old bear called out, 'Halt!'

And the band stopped. Just in time!

THE RAINY DAY

It was raining hard. Jamie and Kate watched as the puddles grew bigger and bigger. 'Can we go outside and splash in the puddles when the rain stops?' asked Jamie.

'Yes, if you wear boots to keep your feet dry,' said their mother.

Jamie and Kate put on their boots.

'My boots are both for left feet,' said Jamie. 'Let's swap.'

'Now I've got one boot that fits and one that's too small,' said Jamie.

Their mother came to help. She sorted out the boots, then took a thick black pen and put big Ks on Kate's boots and Js on Jamie's. 'You won't get mixed up again,' she said. 'Now go and play, before it starts to rain again!'

EARLY-MORNING TED

I love to scramble out of bed
Just as the day is dawning,
To watch the sky turn golden red
While other bears are yawning.
I feel as though I'm Super Ted
At that time in the morning.

IN AN IRISH GARDEN

'gardens where the soul's at ease'
W.B.Yeats

IN AN IRISH GARDEN

Edited by
SYBIL CONNOLLY & HELEN DILLON

Photographs by Walter Pfeiffer

WEIDENFELD AND NICOLSON
LONDON

For Peggy, Judy and John
S.C.

For Val
H.D.

First published in Great Britain by
George Weidenfeld & Nicolson Limited
The Orion Publishing Group
Orion House
5 Upper St Martin's Lane
London WC2H 9EA

Reprinted in 2005

Designed by Helen Lewis

Filmset by Keyspools, Newton le Willows, Lancashire
Printed and bound in Singapore

HALF-TITLE
The graceful stems of *Dierama* arch over a
stone sphinx in Helen Dillon's Dublin garden.

FRONTISPIECE
A long flight of moss-covered stone steps
at Glenveagh Castle, County Donegal.

CONTENTS

ACKNOWLEDGMENTS

The editors would like to thank the following:
Margaret Kennedy, Rosemary Brown, James Sheridan, Laura Turner,
Aidan Brady, Jody Murray, Richard Lowe, Maura Lockhart, Margaret
Morgan, Tim Sharkey, Jolanda Cox, Sean Horace and Peter O'Connor.

Finally, but especially, we would like to thank Wendy Dallas
and Michael Dover for their patience, understanding and graciousness;
without them this book would never have been published.

The publishers are grateful to Donald Church who painted the trophy
reproduced on the endpapers, and to Sally Houseman whose original
pencil drawings of each house appear as chapter heads throughout.

The photograph of Sybil Connolly which appears on page 136
is reprinted by permission of House Beautiful, *copyright © June 1984,*
The Hearst Corporation. All Rights Reserved (photographer Michael Dunne).

In 1983 the Irish State acquired the Castle and lands of
Glenveagh from Mr Henry McIlhenny. They are administered by the
National Parks and Monuments Service of the Office of Public Works,
and are open to the public from June to September.
The Deerpark forms part of the National Park
and is maintained as a Wilderness.

All other properties included in this book are in private ownership
and are opened to the public at the owner's discretion.

FOREWORD
by Sybil Connolly and Helen Dillon

When we agreed to a request from the publishers to write a book on Irish gardens, we both felt that it should be principally about private gardens. There are many beautiful gardens in Ireland which are open to the public. These have been well documented in previous publications; however, many of the gardens included here have never been photographed before, and may well never be again.

It became apparent to us while working on this book that truly dedicated gardeners, unfailingly gracious though many of them have been, do not welcome the invasion of editors and photographers. At a time when armies of labour are a thing of the past, any interruption at the peak of the growing season, preventing them from getting on with their garden jobs, can be a cause of some concern. So perhaps this book will be a unique record of private and individual Irish gardens.

The second point on which we agreed was that the book would cover as wide a spectrum of gardens as was possible in the time allotted to us. So contained in the following pages are gardens which belong to castles, Georgian mansions, small country houses, vicarages, town houses, modern bungalows and cottages in the four corners of Ireland – north, south, east and west.

Had we had more time to spare, we are sure that there are other beautiful gardens in private ownership which we would have wanted to include in this book. As it is, with the interest in plants and gardens increasing at an unprecedented pace, perhaps we have left room for a sequel.

Everywhere we travelled we were received with kindness and patience by the owners of the gardens. There was never a moment when they were less than totally cooperative. For this we were, and are, grateful. This is their book as much as it is ours.

Dublin, 1986

KEY

1 Castletown Cox
2 Graigueconna
3 Garinish Island
4 71 Merrion Square, Dublin
5 Lakemount
6 45 Sandford Road, Dublin
7 Kilgobbin
8 Ardsallagh
9 Glin Castle
10 Hillmount
11 Old Mill House
12 Dargle Cottage
13 Primrose Hill
14 Guincho
15 Stramore
16 Kilbogget
17 Glenveagh Castle
18 Knock-na-Garry
19 Kilmokea
20 8 Clune Road, Finglas
21 Castlemartin
22 Butterstream
23 Charleville
24 Ishlan
25 Beech Park
26 Shiel
27 Coolcarrigan

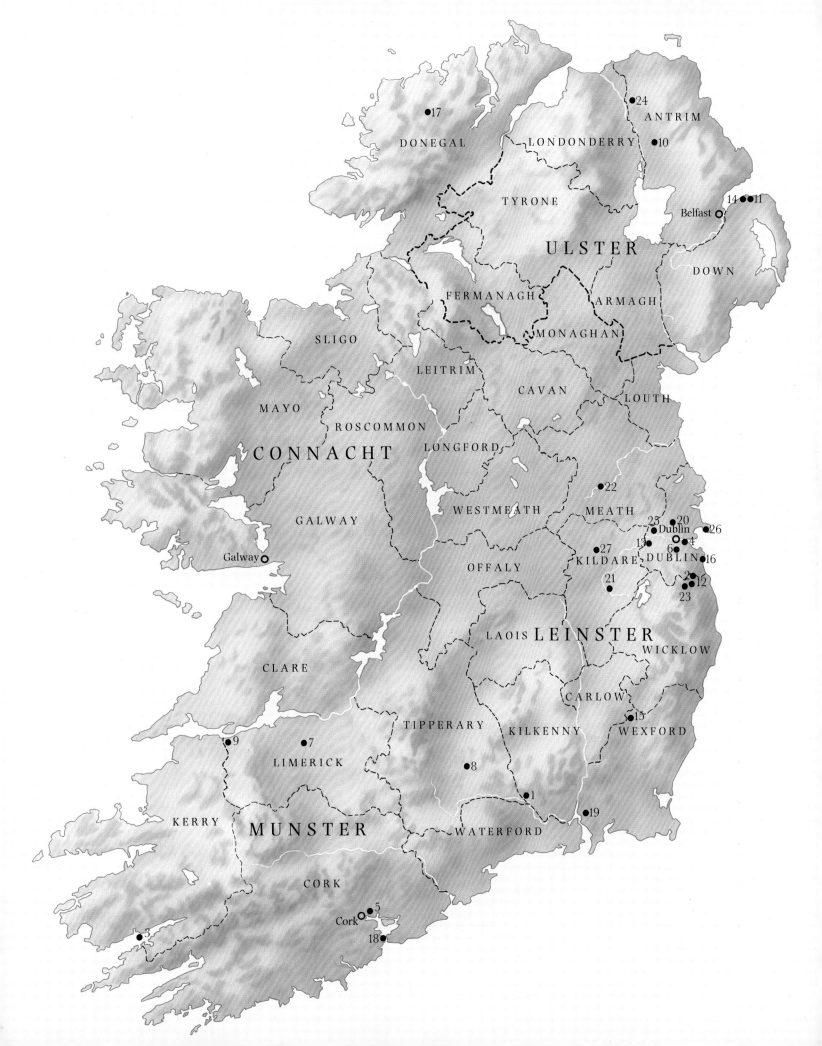

DONEGAL

●17

LONDONDERRY

●24

ANTRIM

●10

TYRONE

ULSTER

Belfast ○

14 ●●11

FERMANAGH

ARMAGH

DOWN

MONAGHAN

SLIGO

LEITRIM

CAVAN

LOUTH

MAYO

ROSCOMMON

CONNACHT

LONGFORD

WESTMEATH

MEATH

●22

Galway ○

GALWAY

25 ● 20

● Dublin ● 26

27 ● 13 ● 6 ● 4

KILDARE

DUBLIN ● 16

OFFALY

21 ●

2 ● 12

23

LAOIS LEINSTER

WICKLOW

CLARE

CARLOW

TIPPERARY

KILKENNY

WEXFORD

15 ●

9 ●

7 ●

KERRY

LIMERICK

8 ●

1 ●

MUNSTER

19 ●

WATERFORD

CORK

5 ●

Cork ○

3 ●

18 ●

PROLOGUE
by Charles Nelson

In an Irish Garden is a celebration of the gardens of Ireland. Through words and photographs it reveals the secrets of twenty-seven gardens, ranging from grand and rugged demesnes in Donegal and Kerry to the plant-rich pleasances of Down and Cork and the trim, compact gardens of Dublin's elegant houses. A few of these gardens are outstanding, historic places developed during many decades and now endowed with features or plant collections of international importance. But the majority are humbler, merely the personal pleasure-grounds of skilful amateurs who began from scratch in recent years and by dint of hard work have created flower-filled oases.

It can be said, with confidence, that a small number of these gardens will survive for many years to come, but, like countless gardens before, the others will only last their creators' lifetimes and will eventually revert to weedy plots or be remodelled and replanted. Yet irrespective of their destinies, the gardens portrayed in this volume are assured of their places in the annals of Irish horticulture because the gardeners who made them have written about them, and the ephemeral grace and colour of each one have been captured on film.

'Secret was the garden, set i' the pathless awe . . .'

Fine gardens do not happen by chance; they have to be ingeniously fashioned. Moreover, the best gardens are much more than neat hedges, weedless paths, colourful flowerbeds and immaculate lawns; they are living, changing communities, managed with care and love by hard-working men and women. Skill and art together are needed to generate from disparate trees, shrubs and herbs gardens that will delight all the senses in every season, and for many generations Irish gardeners have used their imagination to craft beautiful gardens using the best plants made available by plant-hunters and nurserymen.

Gardeners are essentially solitary and secretive. They are happiest when alone, digging in their patch, weeding their flowerbeds, or planting newly acquired treasures. Most of their creations are never seen by the rest of us. Some of the very best gardeners quake even at the thought of someone wishing to visit their secret pleasances, and offer such evasive excuses as, 'It's full of dreadful weeds!' or 'My garden contains nothing that could possibly interest you!' Indubitably the opposite will be found when those timid gardeners relent and allow the stranger to enter their sequestered garths. Yet gardens have always been secret places, the private domains of their cultivators, surrounded by hedges, high walls or moats. The mystery thus engendered is heightened by every gardener's infallible instinct that inside will be found some new and enviable plant. Just as gardeners are secretive, they are also acquisitive, although, to be fair, it is this driving ambition that allows them to enrich their gardens and ensures the survival of the best plants.

The enigmatic quality of each garden owes much to an element of chance which cannot be eliminated, even by the most artful cultivator – the unpredictable culmination of the cycles of growth and flowering that characterize the natural world. No other works of art are as inconstant as gardens, and this surely accounts for the great pleasure that we all gain from gardening.

'Set these against your water-shafted air . . .'

For almost two centuries, Ireland has been held in high esteem as one of the great gardening lands, a place with diversity in garden design, and the cradle of many rare plants. It also has a reputation for being rain-soaked and green, the tell-tale traits of a mild and equable climate.

It is a small island, little more than three hundred miles from north to south and only one hundred miles across at its broadest. The warm waters of the North Atlantic Ocean bathe its shores, and westerly winds which are also warm prevail throughout the year. The westerlies, laden with moisture, can be a hindrance to gardeners living near the coast, but they are essential in maintaining the mellow climate by reducing the severity of frosts. The mean temperature in January is 5°C (41°F) and very few places in Ireland suffer from prolonged periods of freezing temperatures. Snow, if it falls, rarely lies for more than a few days.

There is some variation in the climate between coastal and inland areas, and between the east and west, the north and south, but the differences, which are relatively small – a few degrees and some extra days of frost – do affect the types of plants that can be grown. The coastal fringe is the most favoured, and gardens situated within sight of the sea are virtually free of frost. However, these seaside gardens do suffer from salty winds and gales, and it is necessary to plant shelter belts to protect them from the buffeting westerlies. When shelter is provided, plants of extraordinary tenderness can be cultivated with ease.

Just as Irish winters are mild, so the summers are moist and cool. The mean temperature in July is only 10°C (18°F) above the winter mean, and, as rainfall is almost evenly spread throughout the year, hot, dry spells are unknown.

The soft Irish climate is best understood by comparing it with the climates of places that lie in the same latitudes. The northern extremity of Ireland, Malin Head, is as far north as Moscow which has January temperatures well below freezing and abundant, long-lying snow. The southern part of Hudson Bay is about the same latitude as Ireland, yet permafrost characterizes the surrounding land and ice glazes the surface of the Bay throughout the winter. All the major cities in Canada and the United States are situated to the south of Cape Clear, the southernmost point of Ireland, but many suffer winters that are snow-bound and summers that are dusty and very hot.

'So all agreed through sweet diversitie,
This Garden to adorne with all varietie.'

For more than one millennium gardeners have been aware of the benign nature of Ireland's climate and the fecundity of its soil. The Venerable Bede, who died in AD 735, wrote a chronicle in which he compared early Christian Britain with Ireland, noting that Ireland possessed a milder climate, that milk and honey were readily available, and that there was no lack of vines, which are good indicators of a soft climate as they cannot tolerate frosts at the beginning and end of their growing season.

When Bede was alive the number of different plants cultivated in Irish gardens was small and all were of some use either as food, as sources of fibres and dyes, or as medicinal herbs. Many centuries had to elapse before plants were grown solely for ornament.

By the beginning of the seventeenth century, sweet-smelling wallflowers and gillyflowers and pungent herbs were being planted, but the gardener's choice was still very restricted and almost all the garden flowers were European in origin. However that century saw an influx of North American species. The turn of the century was also marked by the arrival of many southern African plants so that in the early decades of the eighteenth century *Aloe* and *Pelargonium* – now familiar genera – had pride of place in the botanical garden belonging to Trinity College in Dublin.

American plants continued to excite gardeners during the 1700s, but by the closing decades of that century two other regions had begun to yield hardy flowers for Irish gardens. The first Australasian species reached Europe in 1771; many more arrived after the establishment of the convict colony at Botany Bay in 1788. Then began a trickle of Chinese exotics – peonies, roses and plume poppies (*Macleaya*) for example – but that trickle was to turn into a flood just over a century later.

During the nineteenth century, aided by enthusiastic gardener-botanists including James Mackay at Trinity College Botanic Garden and David and Frederick Moore at Glasnevin Botanic Gardens, Irish garden owners obtained more and more floral treasures from far distant continents. They learnt again that Ireland's hospitable environment would allow the cultivation of a multitude of exotic plants in the open air – *Fuchsia*, *Camellia* and myrtles were tried by John Templeton of Belfast in the early 1800s, and other gardeners were successful in later decades with such genera as *Rhododendron* and *Eucalyptus*, and with palms and tree-ferns. The introduction of novel exotics continues today, and year after year we add many new plants to the flora of our pleasure-grounds.

Of course many of the finest garden plants are at least one generation removed from wild species; they are cultivars (cultivated varieties) deliberately bred by horticulturists and then selected for their special qualities. During the last one hundred years, Irish nurserymen have achieved international recognition for prize-winning roses, brooms (*Cytisus*) and daffodils. Other hardy plants – for example cultivars of *Bergenia*, *Primula*, *Dierama* and *Escallonia* – have also carried the substantial reputation of Irish nurseries, including Daisy Hill of Newry, Lissadell of Sligo and Slieve Donard of Newcastle, around the globe, so that wherever good plants are appreciated, the names of those nurseries are familiar.

'Bring roses if the rose be yet in bloom . . .'

Most gardeners, skilful though they be in the arts of planting, pruning and propagating, do not have an aptitude for writing or sketching, the only means by which gardens could be chronicled until the middle of the last century. A simple list of plants does provide the bare bones of a record, and a garden diary gives us the equivalent of a biography. However, without a plan or a sketch it is impossible to reconstruct a true vision of a vanished garden.

The first meagre records of gardening in Ireland come, not surprisingly, from the earliest books. The scribes who copied the Scriptures used colourful inks, some of which were concocted from plants: crimson, for example, was obtained from a plant the scribes called *ru* (probably a form of lady's bedstraw) which they cultivated with considerable care.

In the thirteenth century, roses were added to the assembly of vegetables and useful herbs grown in Irish gardens. On the Feast of the Nativity of St John the Baptist, the traditional Midsummer Day, rents were paid and we know from medieval deeds that payment was sometimes made with root ginger, peppercorns, cloves and flowers. The spices were costly imports, but the flowers that were stipulated in the deeds – chaplets of roses, single rosebuds and even a red rose are mentioned – must have been grown in the gardens of Ireland.

We know very little about the gardens and the gardeners of medieval Ireland, but one did leave a remarkable legacy, a handwritten copy of the first gardening manual in the English language. This takes the form of a long poem attributed to one Master Jon Gardener. Although it was not composed in Ireland, it contains the couplet,

> All of the herbs of Ireland,
> Here thou shalt them know every one.

Master Jon, who was probably a master-gardener in one of the royal gardens near London during the mid-1300s, was a skilful horticulturist and he knew all about the cultivation of vines and vegetables, saffron and rosemary, the sowing of seeds and the cropping of cabbages. He provides in his doggerel verses a long list of herbs that we may safely assume were planted in Ireland's gardens at this period. Jon Gardener mentioned savory, mint, rue and sage, violets and primroses,

> Fennel, southernwood, feverfew and caraway,
> Rose red, rose white, hollyhock and pimpernel,
> All these herbs by Saint Michael
> Must be set in the month of April.

It would be fascinating to know the name of the garden owner who commanded the scribe to copy this poem. We can only suggest that he lived in south-eastern Ireland at the end of the fourteenth century, and that he was one of the Norman settlers, possessing a castle and a walled garden neatly laid out with knots of clipped box.

'Paint as you plant, and as you work design . . .'

The first pictorial representations of Irish gardens date from the early years of the seventeenth century and show that such formal knot gardens were still fashionable. Low hedges of box or lavender formed the pattern and the more colourful flowers were planted in compartments between the hedges. On an early map of Trinity College, founded in 1592 as the sole college in the University of Dublin, knot gardens are depicted outside the main quadrangle. This crude bird's-eye view is not of much value in determining the plants cultivated within the knots, but fortunately the College has kept many of its deeds and accounts, and these provide some fascinating information about its gardens.

The College leased some of its land to the citizens of Dublin, in return for half of the produce harvested. Harry Holland, one of the gardeners named in the College deeds, undertook to dig, prune and plant five gardens with turnips, parsnips, carrots, artichokes, onions and leeks, as well as fruit trees, lavender and roses. He was obliged to provide the cook with sufficient vegetables for thirty scholars; any surplus he kept for his own use.

Other maps made during the early 1600s also show gardens. A plan of Youghal, County Cork, published in 1633, displays a series of knot gardens within the town walls, near the church. A castle garden with clipped trees and knots is depicted on a plan of Limavady, County Londonderry, dating from the same period.

From contemporary manuscripts we can gain a fair idea of the content of the gardens. Dr Peter Lombard, Archbishop of Armagh, commented that the Irish climate was suitable for the cultivation of a wide range of plants, which although not generally grown did better in Ireland than in their native countries. He singled out globe artichokes, squashes and hops, and noted that vines yielded grapes not inferior to those produced in France and Germany. Dr Lombard's contemporary, Philip O'Sullivan Beare, made special mention in his *Zoilomastix* of the cider apple trees grown in Connacht, and of figs and mulberry bushes.

At the close of the seventeenth century, when a wheelbarrow cost sixpence and a spade six shillings, botany and horticulture in Ireland made two important advances. While the kitchen gardens of Trinity College, Dublin, still produced abundant cabbages and artichokes, and the Fellows' Garden was planted with sweetly perfumed stocks and gillyflowers, the College authorities decided to form a botanical garden. That signal event in the history of Irish gardening took place in June 1687.

The second advance occurred a few years later at Moira in County Down, when Sir Arthur Rawdon had a heated conservatory built, the first known to have existed in Ireland. Rawdon was an adventurous gardener who wanted to have something no one else possessed. Not only did he commission the glasshouse, but he despatched a gardener, James Harlow, to Jamaica to collect plants for it. Late in April 1692, Harlow landed at Carrickfergus with twenty cases containing about a thousand tropical plants. The measure of his achievement may be gauged by the fact that no other plant-hunter is known to have brought so many tropical plants alive to Europe until the second quarter of the nineteenth century.

Gardening is not the preserve of men, and many women have contributed to the success of horticulture in Ireland. Lady Helen Rawdon shared her husband's enthusiasm, and undoubtedly helped to care for the Jamaican plants after his early death in 1695. Some of her botanical books survive, including a copy of William Turner's famous herbal with the inscription, 'Hellen Rawdon Her Booke' on its title page.

'Hail, Happy Delville! Blissful Seat!'

The most renowned lady gardener in Ireland during the 1700s was Mary Delany, whose second husband, Dr Patrick Delany, Dean of Down, owned Delville, a small demesne situated about three miles north of Dublin city in the quiet village of Glasnevin.

Mrs Delany was a prolific letter writer and an amateur artist. Her sketches of Delville show an unkempt garden in which was 'Nature improved, and raised by Art'. Despite the herd of eighteen deer which roamed the eleven acres, Delville harboured many flowers. There were orange trees in pots on the parterre around the house. Mrs Delany planted honeysuckle and jasmine, gillyflowers, perfumed roses and primroses. Sweet briers and nut trees lined some of the walks that meandered through the demesne. The portrait that she left of Delville is of a slightly chaotic garden, a romantic 'wilderness of sweets', idyllic and far removed from the staid, formal knot gardens of earlier ages. Mary Delany adored Delville: 'D.D. up to his chin haymaking on the lawn ... and the whole house fragrant with the smell of it ... the garden is Paradisical.'

'Building castles of flowers ...'

Delville was the first choice of the committee charged in 1793 by the Dublin Society and the Irish Parliament with the foundation of a national botanical garden in Ireland, but the demesne was not suitable because the lease stipulated that no trees could be felled. A stone's throw away, across the River Tolka and still within the boundaries of Glasnevin, the committee did find land. On 25 March 1795 the Dublin Society's Botanic Gardens was founded. It was the brain-child of John Foster, the last Speaker of the Irish House of Commons, whose own garden at Collon (County Louth) contained one of the richest plant collections in Ireland. He had almost two thousand different trees and shrubs, but his prize plant was a young shrub of the mudan, the Chinese tree peony, the 'King of Flowers'. John Foster's urge to acquire new plants was tempered by his generosity. He happily sent a cartload of rhododendrons to Maria Edgeworth for her garden, and also gave her an offset of the peony. John Foster and Maria Edgeworth have long since died, but there are still plants of that mudan, direct descendants of the one that grew at Collon, flourishing today. The plant has long outlived the gardeners who first cherished it.

Miss Edgeworth has left us a marvellous if disorderly record of her garden. Her joy shines through. She scribbled new plans in her frequent attempts to improve the garden, and even in her seventy-ninth year she pottered about in it on damp February days in rubber boots, planting new roses. 'I find the love of garden grows upon me as I grow older', she wrote. 'Shrubs and flowers and such small gay things that bloom and please and fade and wither and are gone and we care not for them, are refreshing interests in life.'

She cultivated snowberries and tiger lilies at Edgeworthstown. She also planted a hyacinth named after herself – alas we cannot trace its origins. Roses were among Miss Edgeworth's favourite flowers; she grew damask roses, everblowing roses, 'Maiden's Blush', and that superb pale shell-pink rose with perfect buds, 'Céleste', which is still admired by discerning gardeners. From America Maria Edgeworth obtained the Cherokee rose and a prairie rose, and was amused when the local people re-christened the old pink damask rose 'Quatre Saisons' the Quarter Session rose!

In her children's books, Miss Edgeworth often mentioned gardens, and in *Practical Education*, which she wrote in collaboration with her father, advice was provided on gardening for children. Clearly she loved 'building castles of flowers', and in one of her letters exclaimed how glad she was to 'have acquired this taste for a gay or even a shabby garden – it is a rest to the mind and at all times a relief'.

'Our shadows rove the garden gravel still ...'

We must be grateful to the gardeners of olden days who drew and sketched the gardens they created and bequeathed to us catalogues of worthwhile plants and garden diaries. We must also be thankful that one and a half centuries ago the process of photography was discovered.

One of the pioneers of photography in Ireland was Mary, Countess of

Rosse, whose extraordinary collection of photographic plates is preserved in Birr Castle, County Offaly. She photographed the demesne at Birr, encapsulating its elegant suspension bridge, the bulk of its Leviathan telescope, and the placid lake. One of her photographic portraits records a white-haired old man seated in a leafy bower – the Revd Dr Thomas Romney Robinson, astronomer of Armagh, and the man after whom *Romneya coulteri*, the pure white tree poppy from California, was named.

Lady Rosse's photographic collection is one of the largest that has survived from those pioneering days. By the end of the nineteenth century there were many more people photographing the sites and scenes of Ireland, and by that time too printers had learnt how to use photographs to illustrate books and journals. I cannot be certain when the first photograph of an Irish garden was published, but the *Gardeners' Chronicle* and *The Garden* used photographs to make engravings in the 1880s and by the mid-1890s had started to print them direct. Miss Armstrong's photograph, entitled 'A shady retreat in the Botanic Gardens, Glasnevin', occupied a whole page in the *Chronicle* on 4 April 1896 and is probably the earliest published photograph of the National Botanic Gardens.

In 1900 the rector of Raheny, County Dublin, the Revd F.C.Hayes, illustrated his *A Handy Book of Horticulture* with fine photographs by Greenwood Pim. A sumptuous book, bound in green with gold blocking, entitled *Beautiful and Rare Trees and Plants*, describes Lord Annesley's demesne at Castlewellan, County Down; it was published in 1903. Happily, many of the superb trees portrayed in the full-page photographs still thrive at Castlewellan, which is now the National Arboretum.

That volume was the first book about an Irish garden to be illustrated solely with photographs. A smaller and less lavish book, published in 1927, about the garden at Mount Usher, County Wicklow, was embellished with watercolours by several artists and with views photographed by Elsie Miller, who worked at the National Botanic Gardens, Glasnevin, from 1918 to 1927. Among the hundreds of glass plates still stored in dusty cupboards at Glasnevin are those taken by Miss Miller during the halcyon days of Irish horticulture in the early decades of the present century. But she was not the only photographer working in Glasnevin Botanic Gardens: John Besant, Rosamond Pollock, William Trevithick, G.O.Sherrard and Stephen Rose all contributed to the records of Glasnevin and its plants. The most notable photographer, however, was the Assistant Keeper, Charles Frederick Ball, after whom a blood-red *Escallonia* was named. Was Frederick Ball the person who, in 1911, took the magnificent Lumière Autochrome plates of the immaculate herbaceous borders at Glasnevin, of the *Chrysanthemum* collection and of the scarlet-blossomed *Columnea gloriosa* cascading from its hanging basket? Those transparent glass plates are perhaps the first colour photographs ever taken of the gardens and garden flowers of Ireland. They are also among the finest, because their lustrous quality is rarely equalled even today.

Through photography can be revealed the secrets of gardens, past and present, but the photographs themselves cannot tell the whole story. We still need the written words, for when a photographer exposes a picture, only a minute fraction of a second elapses. If you add together the time represented by all the photographs in this book, you will discover that only a handful of seconds is the total time represented. Yet each and every one of the gardens illustrated has taken years to plant and to mature. These photographs only show moments in the growth of the gardens.

'Harmless I roam amongst the dreams that bloom
In the lost gardens...'

This book, a panegyric on some of the secret gardens of Ireland of the last quarter of the twentieth century, bears witness to the long and distinguished history of horticulture here, and to the handiwork of many gardeners and photographers. We now possess the art and technology to record all our important gardens so that none will disappear and be completely lost. The preparation of chronicles and the assembly of garden archives are urgent tasks well within the competence of every garden owner.

Let us bear in mind the words of Charlotte Grace O'Brien who made a beautiful garden at Foynes, overlooking the broad estuary of the River Shannon, at the beginning of this century. Her garden has vanished, but her published articles and some printed pictures survive. Perhaps her prophecy has come to pass:

> When my bones are dust and my good spade rust, when my house is pulled down and my garden asphalt and brick, my extra special wild briers and my daffodils will still linger on the hillside and scent the bloomy air for generations that know me not, nor mine.

We should not feel too sad that gardens have vanished, for we can still enjoy the plants that they contained and we may, if we take the trouble, read the records that gardeners have left behind. Yet we must not be complacent and allow every garden to fall into ruin. We must strive to preserve the finest gardens that now exist. They are part of our heritage and should remain for future generations to enjoy. However historic gardens must not be allowed to fossilize; their plants have to be renewed so that the living community thrives. When they are tended with love and imagination by gardeners who care deeply about the tradition of gardening in Ireland, our great gardens will keep their enticing secrets and their lustre. When the secrets and the unpredictable beauty are lost, dreams will not bloom.

National Botanic Gardens,
Glasnevin, Dublin, 1986

CASTLETOWN COX
COUNTY KILKENNY
Baron de Breffny

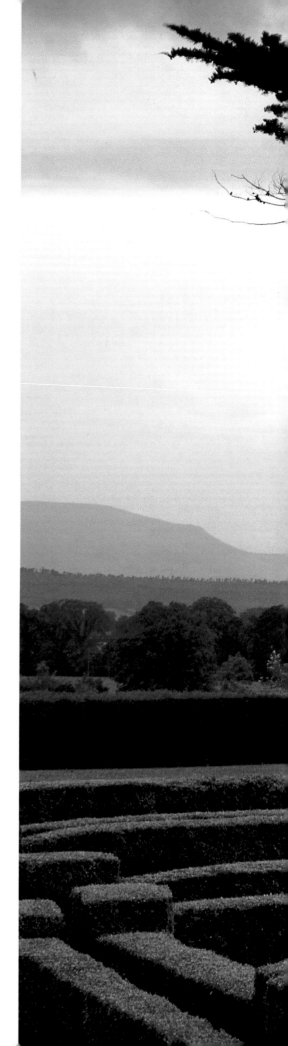

In accepting a kind invitation to write about my garden, I cannot begin otherwise than by saying that although it is indeed our property, I never really think of the garden as *my* garden or *our* garden. However, it certainly *is* an Irishman's garden and has been since Michael Cox, Archbishop of Cashel, planted the demesne in the 1760s and 1770s. I see myself as the custodian, the caretaker, of a garden created before my time.

This role of custodian I accepted happily but not without misgivings. When we acquired Castletown Cox, one of Ireland's most beautiful country mansions, we were immediately more concerned about the upkeep of the pleasure gardens than the maintenance of the house, despite its size (it has twenty-six rooms, and wings on either side of the central block in the Palladian idiom). Prophets of gloom warned us that we would 'never find a gardener'. No gardener myself, I had reason to worry. Several years later, having learned just a little and taken advice from Arthur Shackleton, and with the gardens conscientiously and affectionately maintained by Frank Bradshaw and Michael Walsh, I am relieved to have proved the pessimists wrong.

The pleasure gardens as we found them were much to my own taste: green and grey – hardly a sign of any other colour – very formal, with lawns, shrubs, hedges and statuary. Four handsome, sculpted stone urns are coeval with the house, but the three lead figures were brought here from Clearwell Court in England about seventy-five years ago. At once we added to the statuary, crowning four existing stone pedestals with splendid life-size seventeenth-century northern Italian statues of deities. These we brought to Ireland with immense difficulty owing to their size and weight; on their arrival we had to hire a crane to help unload them and hoist them on to the plinths where they now stand, proudly looking for all the world as if they had been there for ever.

Two straggly herbaceous borders, a late addition which detracted from the forecourt, were soon abolished. Next we enhanced the green-grey tones of the gardens by gravelling the paths. The delivery of the gravel gave me

an idea for coping with the twenty-four compartments of one of the two Edwardian box gardens. This garden, once tended by a man whose sole responsibility it was, used to have bedding-out plants in each compartment to provide a year-round display. I applied weedkiller, carpeted each compartment with black plastic sheeting and covered this with grey pebbles. The effect is excellent and the work saved inestimable. The other box garden, a complicated design of Celtic curlicues, requires much more labour, and although I admire its intricacy I like it less than the more regular geometric one.

The older beeches and oaks were planted in the eighteenth century by Archbishop Michael Cox and his son Richard, whom I bless for these wonderful trees. In them I find an understanding of continuity and even a hint of eternity. The Archbishop also diverted a little stream that flows from the hills behind Owning to create the slate-bottomed ornamental four-acre lake with a little artificial island, inspired by the ancient Irish *crannóg*, or lake dwelling.

The superb *Sequoiadendron giganteum*, 100 feet high and with a girth of 262 inches at chest height, may well have been planted a century ago, but, as this species grows fifty feet or so in twenty years in its native Californian habitat, it is possible that this specimen dates from no earlier than the landscaping undertaken in 1908 by Lady Eva Wyndham-Quin. The handsome stand of Scots pines (*Pinus sylvestris*), the fine Austrian black pines (*Pinus nigra*), the majestic Monterey pine (*Pinus radiata*) and the circle of compact Irish yews all date from that time. It was Lady Eva too who brought the lead statues from Clearwell Court and planted the two box gardens. The architect and garden designer Patrick Bowe has pointed out that Lady Eva's layout followed the style favoured by the Irish-born garden designer Norah Lindsay, who was her cousin and may have advised her.

The extensive walled garden, nearly half a mile from the house, is now part of the farm; beside it are the ruins of the Edwardian rose pergola, from which I salvaged old roses that now flourish on the walls in the forecourt. I am told that it was Lady Eva's pleasure, in those palmy years before the First World War, to have everything white in the walled garden and the farm. Alyssum bordered the paths, white peacocks strutted round the pergola, white doves hovered about a dovecote, the poultry yard had only white fowl, there were only white cattle in the byre. There were white goats imported from the Saanen Valley in Switzerland, white rabbits, white dogs, a family of white cats – maybe even white mice.

We have cleared an invasion of laurel, bracken and *Rhododendron*

LEFT The lake created by Archbishop Michael Cox has been cleared of much of the scrub which surrounded it, providing a clear view from the house. In 1985 this family of eight cygnets was reared on the lake.

RIGHT The formality of the Edwardian box gardens, planted in the Italian style at Castletown Cox by Lady Eva Wyndham-Quin, is a perfect complement to the Palladian architecture of the house.

ponticum, vanquished a horde of determined weeds and re-grassed those lawns on which they had encroached, and planted shrubs, including white-flowering *Viburnum, Eucryphia* and *Magnolia stellata*, and a small arboretum. The old tennis court has been dismantled, its broken surface covered with good soil, grassed and rolled to make a croquet lawn.

A simple, home-made rustic bridge now spans the stream at the foot of the lake, and beside it striking specimens of *Gunnera manicata* brought from Colonel Price's Kilmokea (*q.v.*) have grown to be enormous. Scrubby willows, hazel and some ash have been eradicated from the lakeside to clear the view from the house. In the woodland and around the trees in the park several thousand narcissus bulbs have been put down, mostly pheasant's-eye, paperwhites, 'Fermoy', 'Irish Luck', 'Irene Copeland' and, my favourite daffodil, 'Mount Hood'. Several varieties of *Clematis* planted over the last three or four years are thriving. Unfortunately, Australasian tree ferns from Kerry, which we tried in the woodland, did not survive the harsh winter of 1982.

A sheltered cutting garden has been established for flowers and herbs, with espaliered plum, greengage and pear against the wall. Round this garden we planted a hedge of hornbeam, which is being trained into arches. Beside the back avenue, where trees had been felled, we have set a plantation of over a hundred young oaks and beeches. Three years ago I planted an avenue of a hundred lime trees, which we may not live to see grow tall but for which future generations might bless us.

This written, it occurs to me that we have perhaps done more in six years than I thought. Our major mark on the garden will, however, certainly be the twenty-foot-high sculpture in Spanish chestnut commissioned in 1985 from the Irish sculptor Michael Warren, who has won international acclaim for his work as far afield as Jeddah in Saudi Arabia and Dallas, Texas. Michael studied the garden carefully before choosing a site and has created an exciting non-figurative design to suit it.

GRAIGUECONNA
COUNTY WICKLOW

Mrs John Brown

My first garden was about six feet square and surrounded an old damson tree which never bore fruit. Into this tree grew the climbing rose 'Caroline Testout', and at its foot were candytufts and pot marigolds: I had no eye for colour in those days, and was content just to watch plants growing out of the soil!

This small plot was in my parents' garden at Ballyorney, their Georgian house at Enniskerry, County Wicklow. The main garden was at the back of the house, with a long cinder path leading to an orchard, an unusual feature in Irish gardens; fruit trees were usually planted among the vegetables. On both sides of the cinder path were wide borders, and at right angles was a herb garden with a sundial and a stone seat where you could sit and watch the cloud shadows on the Wicklow Mountains, which sometimes appeared to glow like opals. The orchard was full of ancient apple trees, daffodils and the old pheasant's-eye narcissus.

This, my mother's garden, had an important bearing on my love of plants. She resented any time spent away from it; it was really her life. Her ideas were influenced by Gertrude Jekyll, and her many pen friends among plantsmen included the famous rosarian Graham Thomas and the explorer Frank Kingdon Ward. I remember the excitement when the first flowers appeared on a lily grown from seed that Ward had sent her. Another friend was Lady Moore, wife of Sir Frederick Moore, Keeper of the Botanic Gardens at Glasnevin. She gave my mother the rose 'Souvenir de St Anne's'. A few years ago it was still growing at Ballyorney; I took a cutting from it for my garden here at Graigueconna, and the young plant is now a large shrub.

We moved to Graigueconna in 1970. The garden was started by my great-grandfather, Phineas Riall, in 1830, and his grandson, Lewis Meredith, laid it out as it is today. He turned a long slope into a one-and-a-half-acre rock garden. Huge rocks were moved in trucks, which were pushed along a railway line constructed down the centre of the garden. An alpine enthusiast, he wrote *Rock Gardens* in 1910, which has become a

Rosemary Brown surrounded by the exotic plants that thrive in her conservatory. Above her head hang the deep rose-red flowers of *Passiflora antioquiensis*.

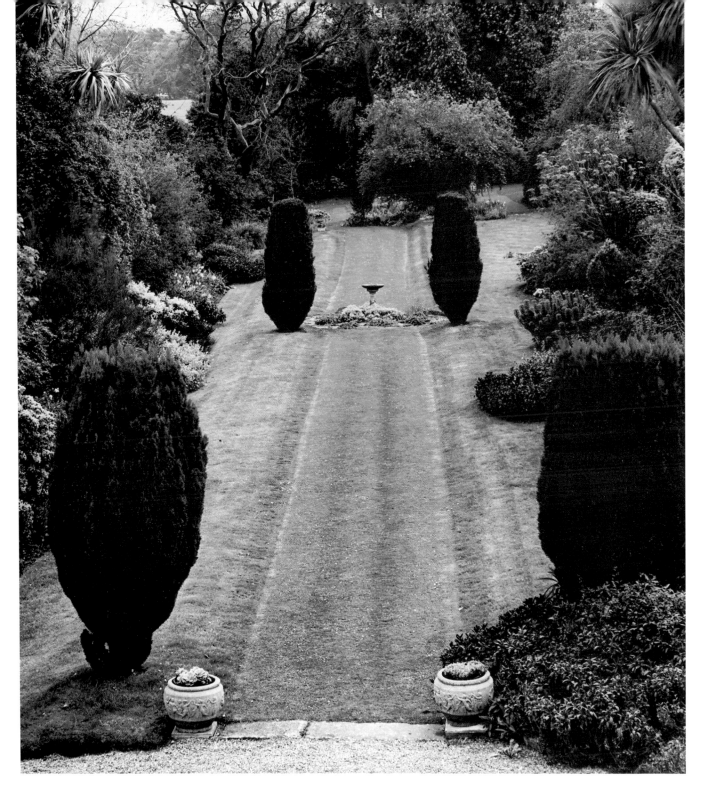

Lewis Meredith's railway line, now a grass-covered path flanked by Irish yews, gives a formal axis to the garden.

gardening classic. When he died the house was let to several families who were keen gardeners, and carried out the same pattern of planting, but when we moved here the house and garden had been empty for several years.

The rock garden had disappeared completely under a blanket of nettles and horsetail – unsuitable bedfellows for alpines! The paddock had been taken over by brambles, which had travelled at a speed only brambles can go. My husband, John, set out with a mattock and saw, and I followed with fork and spade. Within a couple of years the face and paths of the rock garden had been exposed and the paddock cleared. Luckily, the soil was

ABOVE A striking and cleverly orchestrated combination of colours and textures.

LEFT A young *Malus floribunda* in full bloom; the deep carmine buds fade to palest pink as they open, giving this species its incomparably delicate appearance.

ABOVE RIGHT Wild cranesbill, fern and pink *Oxalis* cluster around the base of the strawberry tree's cinnamon trunk.

RIGHT A variegated hellebore, thought to be the only one in existence. It was grown as a seedling from a batch of *Helleborus orientalis* and is soon to be registered under the name 'Graigueconna'.

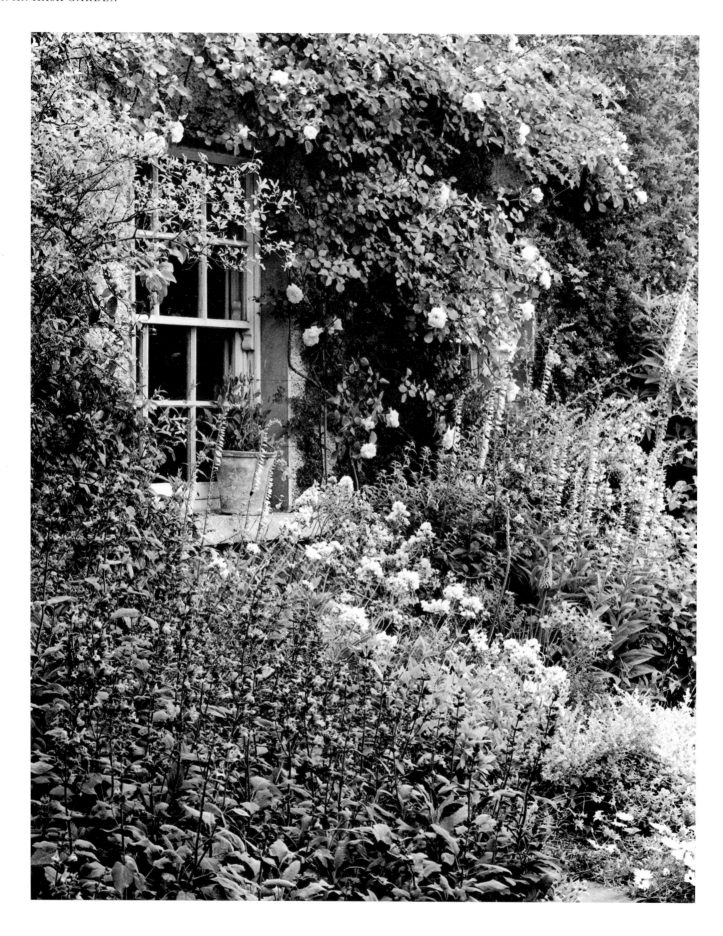

OPPOSITE A border at the back of the house in which purple sage and *Geranium palmatum* mingle with cream foxgloves (*Digitalis lutea*) and tumbling yellow roses.

rich with leafmould built up by years of fallen leaves, and new plants and shrubs got away to a good start. The climate is mild, being close to the sea, though we do get late spring frosts.

We planted the rock garden with sub-shrubs, and such plants as *Dryas octopetala* and *Celmisia*, leaving several pockets for choice specimens. Ferns do well and I have planted aroids and small beds of primulas, including *Primula pulverulenta* and groups of *P. whitei* and *P. gracilipes*. At the back, where the original path winds through rocks and ivy, I grow ferns, *Arisaema* and hellebores. There is a small pool there with a large specimen of the royal fern, *Osmunda regalis*.

The most spectacular sight in the garden is a beautiful hybrid strawberry tree (*Arbutus* × *andrachnoides*) which is eyecatching when its red bark is lit by the setting sun after rain. Another lovely tree, with a shining white trunk, is a Himalayan birch, which is equally attractive in summer and winter. We are lucky to be able to grow both *Acer griseum* – its buff-coloured trunk and branches peel to reveal a rich red-brown bark beneath – and *Acer grosseri* var. *hersii*, a snake-bark maple, which has a green and white striped trunk and attractive leaves that colour well in the autumn.

In the conservatory, which is overcrowded to put it mildly, I grow Australian plants, bulbs, angel's trumpet (*Datura*) and a passion flower that takes over the whole conservatory at regular intervals – *Passiflora antioquiensis*, with rich rose-red flowers.

I collect roses, the species and the old-fashioned cultivars, and have about eighty different varieties. My favourites are 'Céleste', 'Madame Hardy', 'Charles de Mills', 'William Lobb' and 'Madame Isaac Pereire'. Although the flowering season is short, they are so beautiful I feel it is worth every effort to grow them.

Graduating shades of colour give shape and depth in the borders. I like to group tones of pink and blue together, and use primrose yellow to add light. I love pale colours and purple and grey foliage. Large plants of purple sage spaced along the borders leading to the pool carry out this scheme of soft colours. Although I am not keen on large groups of hot colour, pot marigolds and nasturtiums are grown in clay pots near the house. Close by are beds for the treasures which have been given to me by many kind friends. There I can keep an eye on them and protect them from rabbits and vine weevils, the two major pests we have to contend with.

Our garden is about three acres in size and we look after it ourselves, apart from assistance from time to time with hedge-cutting and raking leaves. John spends most of the summer cutting grass and most of the winter making bonfires – and giving me good advice about garden design. Because we have to look after it alone, much of it is really a wild garden into which shrub and old roses, foxgloves and hellebores can grow as they wish.

It is a great joy to be able to work in a garden made with much love by Lewis Meredith. He planned it so skilfully that we have been able, with a few modifications, to follow his original design. I love our garden – especially at dawn when the spiders' webs sparkle with dew, and in the evening as the setting sun lights up the strawberry tree. I cannot imagine life without plants and flowers.

GARINISH ISLAND
COUNTY KERRY

Shamus Browne

There are two Garinish Islands with fine gardens. One is owned by the Irish state and its official name is Ilnacullin; it lies at Glengarriff in Bantry Bay. The second is in Kenmare Bay, and is privately owned. It is this garden that is the subject of this chapter.

Lying off the Kerry coast near Parknasilla, Garinish was bought in 1855 by the third Earl of Dunraven from James Bland, a local landowner who

OPPOSITE, ABOVE The contorted crown of an *Acer palmatum* 'Dissectum Atropurpureum'.

OPPOSITE, BELOW The rounded feathery hummocks of two Japanese maples in the Low Garden. To the right is a fine specimen of *Daphniphyllum macropodum*, whose sunlit young leaves resemble new rhododendron shoots.

RIGHT The brilliant green parasol leaves of *Gunnera* shading bluebells from the sun.

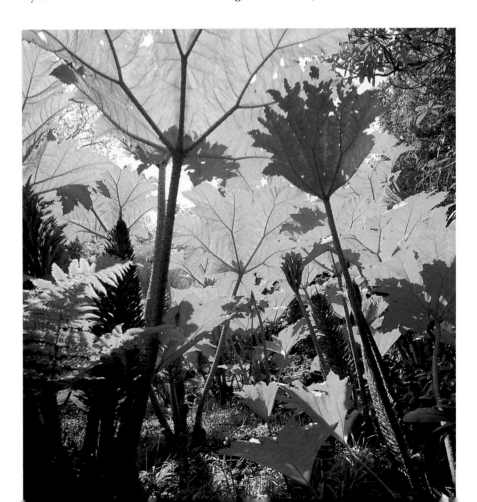

had used the island for grazing his cattle. At that time there was only a cloak of oak woods. Lord Dunraven built a house in 1865, and used Garinish as a base for yachting and archaeological expeditions. While he did plant windbreaks, it was not until 1900 that his son, the fourth earl, began to develop a garden.

A path rambles round this tooth-shaped island, outside the limits of the garden. From this path there are spectacular views, south-west along Kenmare Bay towards Lamb's Head and the Bull and Cow Rocks, and westwards to the MacGillicuddy Reeks. To the east, across the broad expanse of the bay, lie the Caha Mountains.

The island is divided by a series of glens, running from east to west, and separated from each other by high ridges of time-worn rock. These natural valleys were brilliantly used by Lord Dunraven. The glens, sheltered from the wind, were filled with soil laboriously ferried from the mainland, and each one was planted with a rich selection of trees and shrubs, a different genus forming the dominant group in each valley.

Early records tell the stories of these first plants. Some came from Dr Heard of Rossdohan, a nearby island-garden; others were given by Lord Barrymore of Fota Island, County Cork, and the majority were supplied by Thomas Smith's superb nursery, Daisy Hill, of Newry in County Down.

The best way to describe the garden on Garinish Island is to take you on a ramble through the glens. Landing at the pier, after a five-minute boat ride, you will be greeted by a curtain of *Rhododendron ponticum* – sometimes an unwelcome weed in County Kerry, but here forming a splendid windshield, and on sunny days the reflection of its rich purple flowers in the water is quite spectacular.

There is a steep climb from the pier to the house, passing a huge group of *Euphorbia* and a marvellous plant of *Ceanothus* 'Trewithen Blue'. The cream and green foliage of a variegated *Griselinia littoralis* provides a foil for the rose-purple flowers of a Judas tree (*Cercis siliquastrum*). In the small walled garden near the house, a passion flower (*Passiflora caerulea*) and a parrot's bill (*Clianthus puniceus*) tussle for space, and tumble over a fine mixed border of herbs. Around the whitewashed house there is a forest of Californian tree poppies (*Romneya coulteri*), which have gorgeous, silky white flowers with crimson and gold stamens. This is a useful plant as it flowers from July to October and has a delicate yet strange perfume.

There is a winding path from the house to the Palm Garden. Beside a hedge of *Muehlenbeckia axillaris* – normally a creeping, densely matted wiry shrub – we have planted *Puya alpestris*, which has flowers of a unique metallic turquoise blue. Not far away is another Australasian exotic, the pale-yellow-flowered bottle-brush (*Callistemon salignus*), and this provides shade for clumps of dwarf rhododendrons. The Palm Garden is dominated by the hardy Chusan palm, *Trachycarpus fortunei*, and also harbours some of the fine large-leaved rhododendrons, including *Rhododendron macabeanum*, and several large camellias.

On the way to the Low Garden there is a hedge of *Olearia* – one of the silver-leaved daisy bushes from New Zealand – and a shrub of that extraordinary relative of *Ceanothus, Colletia cruciata*. Many of our most unusual shrubs have been planted in the Low Garden. There is also a large dove tree (*Davidia involucrata*), whose white handkerchief bracts flutter from the branches every May. The camphor tree, *Cinnamomum camphora*, provides a large and sombre centrepiece; its aromatic wood is used for furniture in the Far East, but here it is grown for foliage and fragrance. The

The Tree Fern Walk, where fine old specimens of *Dicksonia antarctica* form a canopy over the path.

young leaf rosettes of *Daphniphyllum macropodum* resemble brilliant lime green flowers against the dark, rhododendron-like foliage. Two venerable *Acer palmatum* 'Dissectum Atropurpureum', planted in 1910, have developed into beautiful mounds of finely cut, reddish-bronze leaves. Nearby is an old lily pond, now filled with rich soil, providing a fine bog garden which we have planted with *Astilbe* and candelabra *Primula*. Hostas and skunk cabbages propagate profusely in this hospitable mire.

In contrast to the Bog Garden, one of the most pleasing features of Garinish are the water-worn rocks forming natural rockeries. The immense rock face of the Rock Garden has been colonized by native saxifrages and heathers, and the huge leaves of a spectacular vine, *Vitis coignetiae*, hang jungle-like along the rock edge.

Many of the finest and most interesting plants in our collection come from the southern hemisphere. They revel in the moist and mild climate of Kerry, but would not of course thrive here without the windbreaks. An extensive new windbreak of larch and lodgepole pines was planted in 1970 to supplement Lord Dunraven's original one.

Thanks to this shelter, Garinish Island has a Tree Fern Walk composed of ancient specimens of *Dicksonia antarctica* from Australasia, some growing up straight, others bowed and bent with age. Native ferns, including hart's-tongue and royal ferns have exploited the conditions provided by this marvellous walk, and now there is a thick carpet of many types of fern. Towering above are ancient oaks and several very old trees of *Rhododendron arboreum*, whose red bells drop in showers in the early summer. Another walk, called the Dark Walk, has a dense ceiling of rhododendron branches, curved like the vault of a great church and blotting out the sunshine.

Pine Valley has a magnificent specimen of the Chilean *Podocarpus salignus*, with dark olive green leaves, and a *Bowkeria gerardiana*, an evergreen shrub from Natal, with large ovate leaves and white blossoms in August. *Escallonia* cultivars in pink and white abound. There are many tall eucalypts, and myrtles are now naturalized in the garden.

In the Camellia Garden, which is a marvellous sight in spring, is a plant of *Pseudopanax crassifolius*, with a trunk fifteen feet tall, completely straight and free of foliage. The tuft of leaves on top looks very tropical. Several other interesting shrubs are mingled with the camellias, including *Persea* and the kauri pine (*Agathis australis*). More mundane, but of great interest, is a climbing hydrangea (*Hydrangea petiolaris*), now at least eighty feet up a pine tree.

From the Camellia Garden a path winds through rocky outcrops and a large expanse of *Gunnera*, past some of the largest of our tree ferns and into the Magnolia Garden, which was begun in 1964. All the specimens are flourishing, including *Magnolia campbellii* which has bloomed profusely for the last five years. Mixed with these are other shrubs, including the fern-leaved *Lomatia ferruginea* and *Michelia doltsopa*, a relative of the magnolias.

To walk round the island takes about two hours. To walk through the garden as I have described it would take perhaps forty-five minutes. But it is almost a century since this garden was begun, and endless time is needed to see and enjoy its abundance of good plants.

71 MERRION SQUARE
DUBLIN

Miss Sybil Connolly

I came to live and work in this eighteenth-century house in Merrion Square almost thirty years ago. For reasons which it would take too long to explain, the garden, which joins the main house to the mews in Fitzwilliam Lane, is only twelve years old.

It is a typical town garden in as much as it is long and narrow – 25 feet wide by 109 feet long. All that I inherited was an unkempt lawn and one neglected, overgrown *Philadelphus* which I was reluctant to remove despite its poor condition, but it had to go to make way for the new garden. During the years before work began, this lovely plant exuded a perfume of hope for the future; it was the sweet-smelling 'Belle Etoile' and, to this day, this remains my favourite variety.

With the enthusiasm typical of a new addict, I read every garden book that I could lay my hands on. From the accumulated wisdom of Gertrude Jekyll, Graham Stuart Thomas, E. A. Bowles and others I learned, among other things, that gardens begin with the soil. So, once I had cleared the area, large quantities of the best topsoil were worked into the ground.

Realizing that my most frequent view of the garden would be through the French windows of my bedroom, four floors up, I devised a layout that would be seen best from above. Box hedges are very attractive when seen from this angle, especially in summer when the clipped box is a perfect foil for the relaxed growing habits of the old shrub roses. For a time I seriously considered planting the entire area with formal compartments of box hedges, but finally decided against it. Although it is one of my favourite styles of gardening, it would of its very nature restrict the variety of plants that I could grow.

Keeping in mind the proportions with which I had to work, I decided to divide the garden into three sections. The first area to be planted was that immediately adjacent to the main house, on a slightly higher level than the rest of the garden. Three large niches in the party wall, which might well have sheltered Italian statues or eighteenth-century stone urns in the past, inspired the classical design of the trellis that now covers that wall.

ABOVE A view down the garden, from the terrace to the mews guest house. To the right, beyond the clipped hedges, is a Dr Saunders' hybrid peony, 'High Noon', the only one in Ireland. Beyond the *Choisya ternata* on the right is a standard *Acer pseudoplatanus* 'Brilliantissimum'. To the left of the path, beside the willow-leaved pear tree, *Viburnum plicatum* 'Mariesii' spreads horizontal branches covered in lace-like blooms.

RIGHT The small paved area where spring-flowering bulbs inhabit cracks between the stone slabs. Later the bulbs give way to cinquefoils, sweet-smelling pinks, silver lavender and gold and silver thymes. Grey stone urns and baskets are tightly planted with *Petunia* 'White Joy', and the terrace containers hold cone-shaped box trees. In the central background is a *Eucalyptus maidenii*.

From six zinc-lined containers placed between the niches, clematis, roses, jasmine and honeysuckle climb the trellis, creating a combination of formal and exuberant planting that lasts from April to October. The first rose to bloom in the garden, 'Gloire de Dijon', is planted here. It starts in mid-May, and as I write this, in September, it is still in flower. From my window I can see the much-quartered, pale apricot blossoms looking indeed glorious as they intertwine with the heavenly blue trumpets of morning glory.

Three steps lead down from the trellis wall to a small paved area. In cavities between the old stone slabs, early flowering tulips, crocuses, *Iris reticulata* and other bulbs give great pleasure in the first months of spring. Later, the charming, sweetly-scented old-fashioned pinks bloom contentedly between the paving stones. The African daisy (*Osteospermum ecklonis*) flowers for months on end, as do gold and silver thymes, cranesbills, pink and white lavender, cinquefoils and whatever else I can fit between the stones.

Fortunately, herbs seem to be gregarious, because they have to make do with a herb garden only two feet by six feet! Lovage (for making delicious soups), several mints, French tarragon, lemon verbena and parsley are just a few of the herbs jostling for position in this small patch.

The third and final area of the garden is the largest – the garden proper, so to speak. From the beginning, two good decisions were made about this part of the garden: one was to lay a serpentine brick path through to the mews (this makes the garden appear much wider than it actually is); the other was to plant *Pyrus salicifolia* 'Pendula' halfway down the garden, to the left of this path, giving form to the entire area. Of all the decorative pears, the willow-leaved variety is the most desirable. In my small garden it is pruned in midsummer because by then it looks untidy. It punishes me for this by coming into leaf at least five weeks later than any other in Ireland. When visiting friends' gardens in May I avert my eyes so as not to see their pear trees, already covered in velvet leaves.

There are days when I feel pleased with my garden, and others when I despair. The pleasing days usually last from spring until mid-July. In early June there is a week or two when the garden is a magical place, when the flowering trees and shrubs, deliberately planted so that they complement each other, are at their peak.

The peach-coloured leaves of *Acer pseudoplatanus* 'Brilliantissimum' benefit from being near a bronze-leaved standard *Acer palmatum* 'Dissectum Atropurpureum', with the willow-leaved pear, like a silver-grey crinoline skirt, nearby. A special pleasure are the lavender tulips planted at the base of the tree, which grow at least two feet tall as they strain towards the light.

At this time too, the horizontal branches of *Viburnum plicatum* 'Mariesii' look as though they are covered in white lace. *Choisya ternata*, Mexican orange blossom, competes with a standard tree of double white lilac 'Madame Lemoine' to scent the garden. The lilac-mauve, pendulous racemes of *Wisteria sinensis* cover at least half of the old stone wall on one side of the garden. By a happy coincidence, one of Dr Saunders' hybrid tree peonies, 'High Noon', was planted nearby, its beautiful yellow flowers complementing the wisteria.

I have grown to appreciate increasingly the beauty of the old shrub roses, although perhaps many would think it a little foolish to plant them in such a small garden. They are notorious for their untidy growing habits, and their short flowering season leaves one with rather unattractive shrubs

Sybil Connolly and the moss rose 'William Lobb' in late June. Beside it are the enormous pink blooms of the modern shrub rose 'Constance Spry' and the older 'Fantin Latour', both underplanted with long-spurred columbine. In the foreground is a small standard *Acer palmatum* 'Dissectum Atropurpureum'.

A nineteenth-century plaster bust on a plinth of Coade stone stands in a niche framed by the ornamental trellis. The fat white buds of *Clematis* 'Madame le Coultre' intertwine with the rose 'Madame Alfred Carrière'.

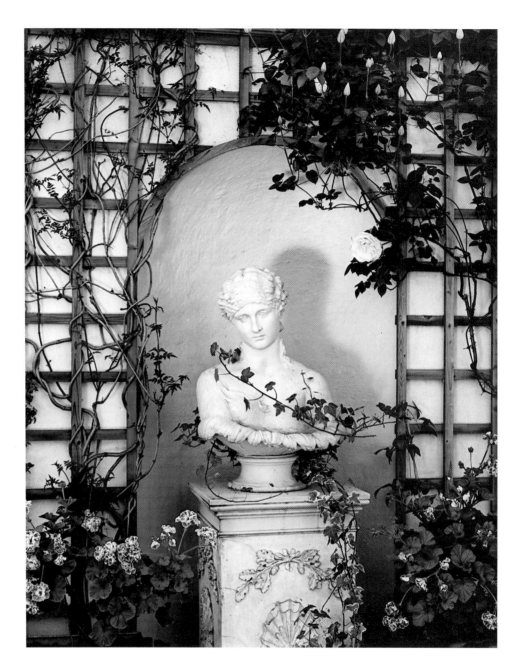

for almost ten months of the year. But when in bloom they are such a joy to behold that I feel they are worth any inconvenience.

One of my favourites is 'William Lobb'. The first flowers are a deep crimson. Slowly they turn to mauve and finally, before dying, to the most exquisite colour – almost a lavender-grey. One day last summer I took the trouble to count the blooms on 'William Lobb': excluding buds, there were 174. The striped rose 'Variegata di Bologna' is another favourite; it reminds me of the roses in medieval tapestries. 'Caroline Testout' must surely be everyone's dream of what a perfect pink rose should look like. There are quite a few French Madames – 'Madame Isaac Pereire', 'Madame Pierre Oger', 'Madame Alfred Carrière', and others – whose names read like heroines from a nineteenth-century French novel. We are encouraged to grow *Rosa glauca* for its foliage alone; the small pink blossom is dismissed as being too 'modest'. For my own part, I find this little flower

The pale apricot tea rose 'Gloire de Dijon' climbing the trellised wall next to the main house, with the creamy white blooms of 'Madame Alfred Carrière', *Jasminum officinale* and the yellow rose 'Golden Showers'. In the foreground is the spectacular *Clerodendrum thomsonae*, brought out of doors in early summer, having wintered inside.

rather endearing, and all the more so for being faint-hearted in the company of her more exuberant sisters.

Many plants share the beds with the roses: the invasive but irresistible lily-of-the-valley, double white campanulas, columbines, white, pink and red poppies and the brilliant blue *Meconopsis* 'Slieve Donard'. *Viola* 'Irish Molly' (my current favourite, which has a distinct if faint fragrance), grows here alongside several hellebores, of which I have a high opinion as they compose themselves beautifully in the dark, damp places of the garden which most other plants will not tolerate.

I learned a little Latin when I was young, so Latin names do not present a problem. However, in some cases I think the English name can be more attractive. For example, columbine sounds nicer than *Aquilegia* and foxglove than *Digitalis*. Anyhow, who am I to quarrel with someone as august as Vita Sackville-West who wrote that she would much prefer to call a plant 'Bouncing Bet' than *Saponaria officinalis*!

I do not scorn annuals. One thing I like about them is that they have to make the most of their short lives by being bright and cheerful from the beginning. In late summer I am grateful to have *Nicotiana*, especially the lime green varieties, to fill in gaps. They look wonderful planted next to the chocolate-coloured and chocolate-scented *Cosmos atrosanguineus*. White petunias I grow from seed, and then plant them very close together in grey stone urns. They last from June until September.

Early on in the life of my garden I realized that the hands of a designer are not compatible with those of a gardener. In order to have the best of both worlds, I resolved to wear gloves when working with the soil. Each March, around the time one becomes active in the garden, I sally forth armed with trug, secateurs, trowel, and whatever other tool I think I might need. Invariably, within half an hour I have met my first reluctant weed; off come my gloves, and off they remain until October. The interim months are spent sitting on my hands and hoping that people will not notice the pieces of soil which seem reluctant to leave my fingernails!

One of my regrets in life is that the demands of my career are such that I do not have as much time as I would like to work in the garden. Without the help of James Sheridan (who also helps me run my household), the garden would not be as it is. He has a natural feeling for things which grow in the soil.

Gardens can never remain the same; they must have a future as well as a past and a present. Good plant association can vastly improve the appearance of one's garden, and I now long to dig up the entire herbaceous garden and move plants to where they will enjoy more complementary companions.

Another plan for the near future is to turn the small garden behind the mews into a knot garden. Already I am drawing plans on odd scraps of paper as to where the box should be planted. And what shall I plant inside the hedges I wonder? Perhaps tulips for the spring? Old roses and lilies for the summer? Dreams, all dreams . . . but then everyone must have a dream, and a garden is as nice a thing to dream about as almost anything else.

LAKEMOUNT
COUNTY CORK

Brian Cross

We bought Lakemount, a former chicken farm, in the early 1950s. Our only inheritance apart from chicken wire, which after thirty-five years we are still removing, was a handful of plants such as *Magnolia* and *Embothrium*. The advantages of the rich, acid soil and the south-facing slope were tempered somewhat by our location on the crown of a hill, exposed to winds from the north-east. A shelter belt of conifers, planted early on, was blown down in the winter of 1972. We thought it was the end, but after weeks of cutting timber, and dragging away scrub, that not untimely wind was the begetter of the present garden.

We were fortunate in having a gardener then, and with his assistance a series of low stone walls was constructed and a pond dug; then a second one. Now we have combined the two ponds and have noticed, with a larger area of water, the importance of reflections of the sky, of distant foliage and even of individual plants. But a shoal of goldfish in the pond provides an irresistible attraction for the local heron.

Visitors to the garden see first a specimen of *Osmanthus delavayi*, a good shrub to liven up a corner in spring, with neat evergreen leaves and fragrant white flowers. Beneath it nestles a clutch of cyclamen.

The lawn was cut from a rough field and thus contained moss and weeds, but by using selective weedkillers it has been transformed into a respectable piece of turf. To the east of the house, grass is confined strictly to narrow paths winding through a maze of interlocking beds.

In one bed the scarlet and crimson flowers, fruit and foliage of *Photinia villosa*, *Clematis* 'Niobe', *Geum rivale*, *Arctostaphylos nevadensis* and *Berberis thunbergii* combine and contrast in the centre of a large group of camellias. A moist island bed, extending into the shade, is the chosen area for some unusual species: the rare South African rope grass, *Restio subverticillatus* (ours is a piece of the original specimen from Fota Island, County Cork), *Brachyglottis*, *Dicksonia antarctica* and the Japanese banana thrive here. These plants have to be swaddled in winter and remain so until March at the earliest – the only plants that demand, and get, this kind of attention.

OPPOSITE, ABOVE Brian Cross and his dog Meggie by the summerhouse.

OPPOSITE, BELOW Spreading across an urn-topped gatepost are the white-splashed leaves of *Actinidia kolomikta*. On the right the horizontal branches of *Viburnum plicatum* 'Mariesii' hold up clusters of white flowers.

The southern hemisphere is further represented here by *Dianella tasmanica* and the lush Chatham Island forget-me-not, *Myosotidium hortensia*. The pale yellow globes of *Rhododendron macabeanum* are reflected by the handsome gold-splashed leaves of *Aralia elata* 'Aureo-variegata'. The Japanese giant heliotrope *Petasites japonicus* is surrounded but not so far contained by *Symphytum × uplandicum* 'Variegatum' – a planting we have not had time to rue! Forgotten offsets of *Cardiocrinum* push up among the felted underleaves of *Rhododendron sinograde*, now flowering after a wait of six years. Gardening imposes patience, and it is better to give in gracefully at the start. An impatient gardener is a contradiction in terms.

The conservatory entrance is flanked by a pair of terracotta cylinders with raised figures like a Greek frieze, planted with two clipped *Lonicera nitida* 'Baggesen's Gold', echoing the formality of two *Acer pseudoplatanus* 'Brilliantissimum' in the courtyard. Inside, one's first impression is of fragrance, for here are scented flowers and foliage in plenty: *Datura*, *Pelargonium tomentosum*, *P. crispum*, *Rhododendron* 'Fragrantissimum' and

ABOVE A spectacular display of azaleas backed by *Aubrieta*, which helps to clothe the grey stone walls throughout the garden.

LEFT *Fuchsia* in a terracotta pot, *Clematis* 'Ville de Lyon' and *Itea ilicifolia* outside the conservatory.

A small stone cherub among huge
hydrangea heads.

'Lady Alice Fitzwilliam', their scent contained and intensified within the
four walls, all contribute to the pot-pourri. The eye is attracted by unusual
climbers like *Sollya heterophylla* and *Dendromecon rigida*, and the foliage of
Helichrysum petiolatum 'Limelight' and a splendid *Cyathea*. A semicircular
pool against the back wall, fed by water from a stone lion mask, contains
tender water lilies, and *Lobelia cardinalis* which grow actually in the pool.

The summerhouse by the swimming pool is a haven of warmth long into
a sunny summer's evening. A lead figure, rescued from a demolition site,
rests here between marble columns. We can never resist an offer of material
that might be of use.

The garden is never static. Apart from the seasonal changes, and the
increasing stature and maturity of the plants, new acquisitions are
continually being made and new plans devised. Currently the sod is being
removed for a new island bed where we hope to create foliage contrasts in
yellow and white using *Phormium* 'Yellow Wave', *Miscanthus*, *Celmisia*,
Kniphofia 'Little Maid' and several other species. At the same time seed is
being sown to increase the drifts of polyanthus, which form a rich carpet
and are the nearest we approach to bedding out plants. This year a young
Beschorneria is putting up a flowering spike for the first time. These small
pleasures add up to a very pleasing whole.

Brian Cross.

45 SANDFORD ROAD
DUBLIN

The Hon. Mrs Val Dillon

It is often said that there are two types of gardener, collectors and makers of garden pictures. I can never decide which I am. In the end, the plant must come first, and if it can be placed where it is going to look pretty as well as thrive, so much the better. Deciding where to plant is, to me, the most important part of gardening. Sometimes this decision has been made, the bucket of sieved leafmould prepared and, at the last minute, it occurs to me that nearby plants are too invasive, the position unsuitable after all, and back goes the plant to the potting shed.

When we moved here twelve years ago, to a typical, pleasant Dublin garden, I had the usual new garden owner's attitude of not daring to touch anything: my courage failed me when it came to pruning the established apples and pears in case of damaging them; if I dug up a bluebell by mistake, it was carried tenderly down to the end of the garden and replanted. I now say, 'Death to bluebells' and pull their heads off to stop them seeding, for no matter how lovely they are in woods, in an overcrowded town garden they are a nuisance.

I started to change the garden piece by piece, and the process continues. Every spring it is satisfying, as all gardens should be, but by late July all the mistakes show. New paths and beds are made – endless alterations take place. So many visits have now been made to the builders' merchants to buy sand for the raised beds and paved paths that the rather taciturn man there just looks at me and shouts, 'Three bags of sand'.

The longer one has owned a garden the more complicated it becomes to find appropriate sites for all the good plants that have to be accommodated; they cannot all have first-class positions, and fitting them all in is like doing a jigsaw puzzle. I think it is easier to go against all gardening rules and change many of the beds in August, when I can see exactly what colour and size the plants are. The beds may appear empty in winter, but what looks like a lovely gap in full sun turns out to be starved of light and moisture in summer. So plants are moved in August – very carefully – and are planted with a bucket of what I think they would fancy. Any

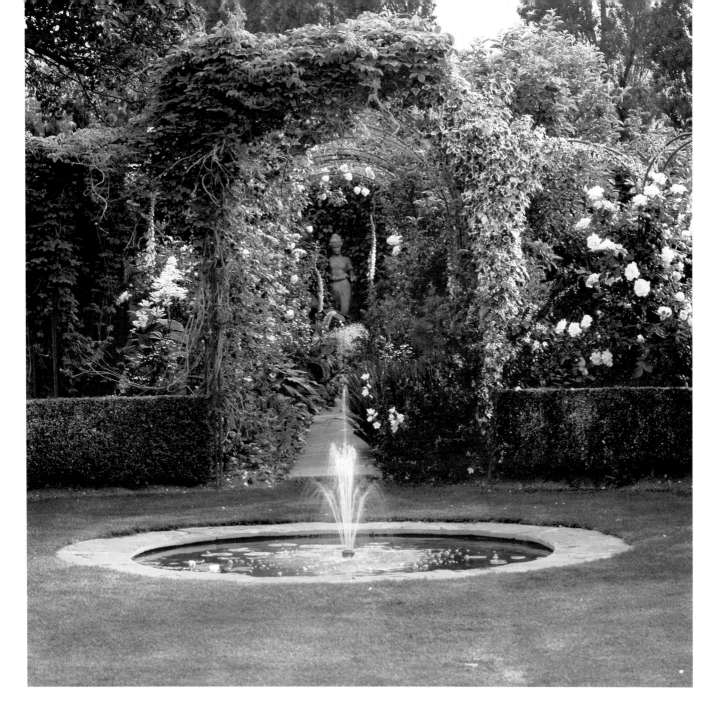

ABOVE A bower of mixed roses beyond the fountain.

OVERLEAF LEFT The garden in midsummer. On the right a *Cornus controversa* 'Variegata' spreads its pale, layered branches opposite a *Robinia pseudacacia* 'Frisia'.

OVERLEAF RIGHT A benign sphinx guards antique terracotta baskets full of tulips and forget-me-nots on the sunken terrace.

combination of peat, leafmould, old manure, compost, fresh topsoil, sand, bonemeal and a balanced fertilizer is used; perhaps the maternal instinct in women activates the desire to feed plants well.

My front garden is not a good place for plants. It faces north, and the soil is thin, poor and badly drained. Unfortunately, it is overlooked by passers-by, so to qualify for a position here, plants must be sturdy and must not require staking, watering in drought, dead-heading or spraying. We inherited a large cherry, which looked heavenly for two weeks in February, but its suckering roots spread far and wide; it has now been removed, making space for a good-sized bed. A load of limefree topsoil was ordered, and gardeners now mutter, 'Virgin soil' when they go by, as plants do so well in it.

There are some special plants here, including hardy orchids, *Roscoea*, and the Japanese painted fern *Athyrium nipponicum pictum*, its silver fronds suffused with purple. Silver- and blue-leaved plants lighten up this shady

bed – *Celmisia*, *Astelia*, *Rubus thibetanus*, *Salix helvetica* and *Potentilla* 'Vilmoriniana', one of the prettiest cinquefoils, with silvery leaves and pale primrose flowers. *Dicentra* 'Stuart Boothman', *Hosta × tardiana* 'Halcyon', *Berberis dictyophylla*, *Acaena* 'Pewter' and *Veronica perfoliata* are some of the blue-leaved species. Blue and white *Viola cornuta* run through and around the other plants, and for early spring there is a good large snowdrop with wide, glaucous leaves, probably *Galanthus elwesii*.

The idea of 'garden rooms' may now be a cliché. I do feel, however, that it is a shame to see the whole garden at once; one needs many different aspects and varieties of soil condition to accommodate a fine diversity of plants. It grates on my nerves to see plants from different native habitats growing side by side. I have therefore made raised beds that cater for the needs of a wide variety of plants, either in full sun, with a well-drained mixture, or partly shaded, with a lime-free, peaty mixture that I try and keep damp in summer. The impossible conditions to provide here are moist soil with full sun. When the books say a plant demands this I pace the garden in a state of indecision.

It is a struggle to grow the loveliest of the woodland plants in relatively hot, dry Dublin soil. But some are worth any amount of effort, and shady beds are a must for blue poppies, ferns, primulas, *Disporum*, *Arisaema*, toad lilies and the very beautiful *Glaucidium* and bloodroot. I am always interested in finding good, worthwhile plants that will readily accept second-class positions, and I suppose that is why hostas, hellebores and cranesbills are so unfailingly popular. I have to admit I love them too.

I enjoy weeding. Each weed removed is ultimately time saved. I do not really mind them individually, but the thought of their myriads of seedlings hardens my heart. Weeding keeps one in close contact with the plants, drawing one's eye to any that need attention – feeding, propagating, or rescuing because they are getting squashed. If I can really control the weeds in May, the rest of the summer is much easier. In my early days I thought pearlwort was a moss, and thought it looked rather charming running between paving stones, but I have discovered what an insidious little brute it is. Weeding underneath hostas is particularly soothing: a wonderful green gloom is created by the light shining through their leaves.

Early June is the only time when I can get relief from the rush to keep up with the work. Then so many plants look their best, dead-heading has not started, the first flushes of weeds have been dealt with, and watering has not begun in earnest. Dead of winter is my other favourite season – plenty of time to stand and stare. But best of all is the sight of heavy rain after drought.

Visiting other gardens is an essential occupation for a good gardener. There is no garden in which there is nothing to learn. The 'pecking order' that establishes itself on these visits has always amused me. After a polite lunch, the host leads the way and the most knowledgeable gardener among the guests follows directly behind. I sometimes find myself at the end of the line, and my attempts to get nearer the front, to hear the discussion about the treasure in question, are thwarted.

Sometimes when taking visitors round my own garden, I realize we have come to a halt near a particular plant. They stare at it in silent contemplation and do not seem to want to move on. This means they would like a piece, but are too polite to ask.

I have some rare plants, but for me a worthwhile plant must be beautiful as well as rare. I am beginning to understand why some plants are scarce. They may be difficult to propagate, or given to what the Irish call 'going for their tea', in other words, dying for no apparent reason. I cannot stand the sight of dead bodies round the garden – such an affront to one's skill. I get rid of them immediately and keep on trying. Sudden death is forgivable; refusing to grow is intolerable.

All my beds are mixed, very mixed – shrubs, herbaceous plants, roses and bulbs – and it is a matter of fitting them all in somehow. When I try to describe the occupants of a bed, it sounds like a description of people at a party: *Cornus controversa* 'Variegata' wore a delightful layered skirt in pale

LEFT Helen Dillon.

RIGHT The yellow form of *Fritillaria imperialis* (crown imperial), a member of the lily family from the Himalayas. Clusters of bell-shaped flowers are carried on stems up to three feet high.

green and cream, while *Convolvulus elegantissimus* was running about, as usual, in silver and rose pink, behaving badly and elbowing her neighbours out of the way. The ragwort 'Desdemona' sulked because there wasn't enough to drink; 'Fusilier', a dashing tulip, was kitted out in brilliant scarlet. Everyone thought *Daphne cneorum* 'Eximia' looked decidedly off colour, and had probably caught a mysterious disease from her cousins. All the poppy family were there: *Romneya coulteri* in translucent white; *Stylophorum diphyllum* arrived early; *Meconopsis* 'Slieve Donard' came in an incredible blue dress, and the opium poppies produced so many children that there was hardly room for anybody else.

Some flowers I just cannot resist – red-hot pokers for example. But nature itself curbs unbounded enthusiasm. I collected innumerable species of *Allium* until they got onion neck rot, every available cultivar of *Iris reticulata* before they succumbed to inkspot disease. And the vine weevils loved best of all the fleshy roots of my collection of *Sedum*, so they perished too. And now? I am rather fond of *Origanum*, but hardly dare write that for nothing has attacked them yet.

Garden work is never ending. Nonetheless, throughout the year there are unexpected, bewitching moments when I glimpse perfection, and all my efforts are rewarded.

KILGOBBIN
COUNTY LIMERICK

The Dowager Countess of Dunraven

My garden. How can I begin, except at the beginning, in 1934, when I had the good fortune to marry an Irishman and came to live in Adare. I remember well the first time I saw the house that was to be my home. It was not in the Adare Manor demesne but nearby, down what was then a little country road. A sudden turn revealed a straight driveway, bordered by huge and ancient oaks arching majestically overhead, allowing only a peep at a welcoming little yellow house.

The brief history of this house began in 1777 when Sir Richard Quin (later first Earl of Dunraven) married Lady Muriel Fox-Strangeways, daughter of the first Earl of Ilchester. Richard's father gave him Kilgobbin, where the couple lived until he inherited the Adare property.

History was to repeat itself, when in 1934 my husband's father gave Kilgobbin to him. During the intervening years it had become known as the Dower House, and had been lived in by various relations and friends of the family. When we arrived it had no pretensions and little comfort (not even electricity) and no garden – but the eighteenth-century builders had left some hallmarks of the period on the little house.

Our first move was to acquire a gardener, Dick Heavener by name, who turned out to be one of the best. He trained many young gardeners over the years, one of whom, Pat Hennesy, a worthy disciple, was eventually to succeed him.

Directly behind the house there was a walled-in square of about two and a half acres, with little else but a few apple trees. My enthusiastic husband and I, together with Heavener, planned a garden. We divided the square into six squares, with four wide paths intersected by four narrow ones. Each square was then bordered with espalier apples, planted with vegetables and soft fruits, like some of the gardens of France. Along the main paths, underneath the apples, we planted flowers – all our favourites, roses, peonies, poppies and lilies. By the smaller paths we put in tulips and narcissi for spring, and pinks and pansies for summer.

I spent many happy hours in the garden, dead-heading, tying up and

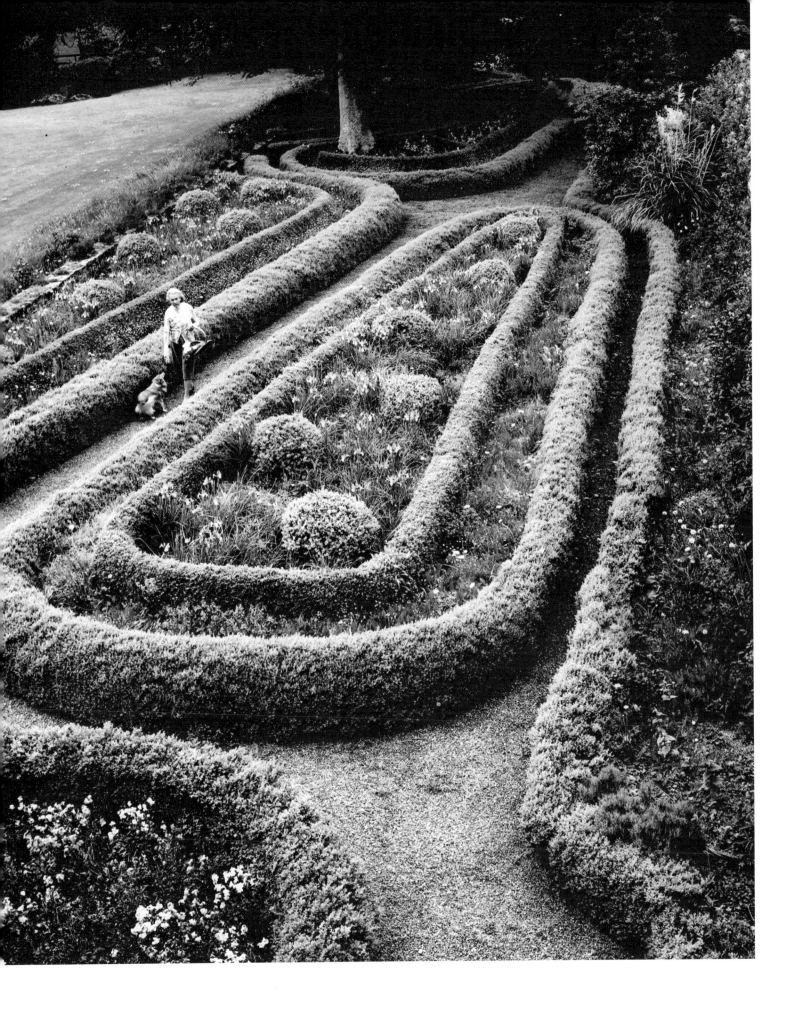

PREVIOUS PAGE Rivers of forget-me-nots swirl round islands of wallflowers in the box garden, shaded by ancient and beautiful beeches.

OPPOSITE Nancy Dunraven in the box garden, planted here with masses of pale blue iris and bluebells; round clumps of variegated box provide a contrast of shape and colour.

cutting down – all the little nanny jobs. Just working away in this fashion helped me through some of the cloudier moments of my life. Gardening has a way of doing that for you.

For a time I had been wondering what I could do with some rather oddly shaped flowerbeds, whose stone edges were infested with weeds. One day I was walking through the Adare Manor woods and noticed some fine big box bushes. On the spot I decided to turn my ugly beds into a box garden, so the never-daunted Heavener paid a visit to the Manor woods, and came back with a vast number of cuttings.

We started with a single edging, but had enough box to plant a further

The garden room, where cut flowers are arranged for the house.

row inside. We then put in forget-me-nots close together, and now in spring it looks like a little stream running between two green banks – at least I think it does. We have let the hedges grow quite tall, as they do in Virginia, rather than in the style of the old English knot gardens. Lately I have planted some rather splendid balls of variegated box in a few of the beds, and also the blue Spanish iris which comes through year after year.

In the box garden, along the back of the old garden wall, is a border of flowering trees and shrubs, with a colour scheme of green, yellow and white. There are silver and golden variegated hollies, the waving, graceful white plumes of pampas grass, *Hypericum*, *Helleborus corsicus*, *Sarcococca*, and best of all *Phlomis fruticosa*, the Jerusalem sage, with silver, velvety leaves and a strange, attractive golden flower.

A deep border of trees and shrubs, again chosen for colour and shape, fills the end of the south-west lawn. I can see it from my bedroom window, and at all times and seasons there is something there to brighten the day.

Round a curve of the path nearby are old French roses, underplanted with peonies. They are a joy during the summer, with their delicious scent and romantic names. The Rugosa roses rival them nearby – the pink and purple and, best of all, 'Blanc Double de Coubert', which with a few Regale lilies forms a frame round an enormous white wooden bench. It was made some years back by our house carpenter, from a photograph of the Chinese Chippendale bridge which spans the lake at Pusey in Wiltshire. I often sit here in the spring, looking at the house through the groups of *Prunus* 'Tai Haku', their branches laden with bouquets of white blossoms.

The path leads on to the Apple Tree walk, the result of my attempts at landscape gardening in 1938. It is a beautiful tunnel, all pink and white at apple blossom time.

Just before the Second World War we went to shoot at Castle Forbes in County Longford. One evening Lady Granard took me round the gardens – and beautiful they were – but above all my eye was held by a group of large oak trees, and underneath them a luxurious blanket of hundreds of little mauve and white autumn *Cyclamen hederifolium*, to me a very exciting sight. And the sequel was just as exciting: next day, when we arrived home, I found a wicker basket in the boot of the car, brimming over with the plants.

Remembering how happy they had been beneath the oaks at Castle Forbes, it was obvious where we should plant them. We divided them into fifty small clumps, one for each of Sir Richard's now very old oaks along the drive. They must be equally happy here as they have never asked for help – yet – and have spread in an amazing way, encircling every tree and even climbing along the banks under the privet hedges. Every autumn I wonder if it can happen again.

I think there should be a mention of the daffodils which line both sides of the drive while the oak trees are still bare, showing that spring is really on the way.

Nancy Dunraven

ABOVE A hedge of sweet peas in shades of pink and mauve near the house.

RIGHT Leading to the house is an avenue of oaks underplanted with autumn-flowering *Cyclamen hederifolium*.

ARDSALLAGH
COUNTY TIPPERARY

Mrs Betty Farquhar

The land in Tipperary is reputed to be some of the best in Ireland. The stiff yellow clay is difficult to work but is rich, leaving little to be done by way of preparation; it is also neutral and retains moisture well. Ardsallagh is situated in the middle of Tipperary, in the 'golden vale' famed for its dairy herds. When I bought the house in 1949, it was inhabited by hens, encircled by laurels and surrounded by open fields. An enormous walled garden behind the house sheltered nothing more than grazing horses and apple trees. I proceeded to clear the ground of laurels, tree stumps and old tins – and started to plant.

While the builders were renovating the house, they helped me to lay a large courtyard at the back of the house with Liscannor stone; I used the biggest possible slabs as they were the cheapest. This provided a sheltered bay where I could grow tender plants against the sunny walls of the house. I urgently needed some height, so I planted *Eucalyptus dalrympleana*, which has beautiful peeling bark. *Acacia pravissima*, a graceful mimosa, grows on the walls, alongside both the blue- and white-berried forms of *Billardiera longiflora*. *Bomarea caldasii*, a handsome cousin of *Alstroemeria*, climbs to twenty feet each year, but dies to the ground every winter. *Mutisia oligodon*, its lax stems supported by a wire cage, is hardy in the open courtyard, but the rare *M. decurrens*, whose brilliant orange daisies used to gleam from the sheltering house wall, has now sadly died.

The arching flower stems of *Beschorneria yuccoides* from Mexico are complemented by the Liscannor paving, now mellowed by the lichens which flourish in the pure air. Apparently this giant is now rare in the wild: goats enjoy eating the seed. When it starts to bloom a wonderful salmon pink stem erupts from a bud huge with promise. The flowering spikes gradually extend until they are eight feet tall and then emerald green bells emerge from rosy bracts.

A wrought-iron gate in the wall of the courtyard leads on to a large lawn, surrounded by a formal hedge of Lawson's cypress. This hedge was planted for shelter as the house is on top of a hill, exposed to every gale. I have

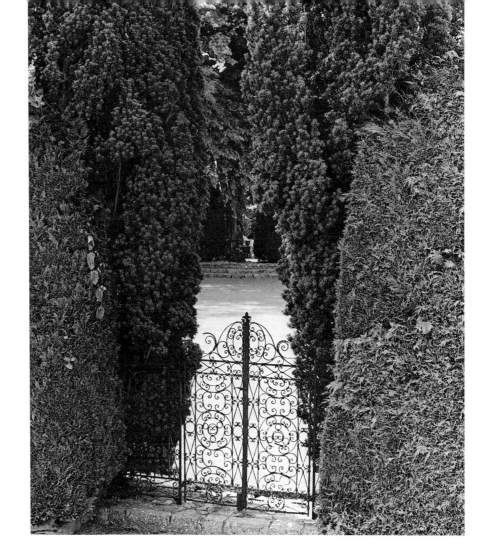

Pillars of Irish yew flank a wrought-iron gate that leads to an uncluttered expanse of lawn hedged with Lawson cypress.

Betty Farquhar framed in an arch leading to the herbaceous garden.

managed to resist the temptation to clutter the plain expanse of grass with other plants, as it shows off the house and solarium that overlook it. However, there are a few beds near the solarium which are filled with favourite plants, including the grey, prickly-leaved *Argemone mexicana*, whose poppy flowers have petals of luminous white silk. There is a fine specimen of *Fascicularia bicolor*, fully six feet across; pale blue flowers form in the base of the leaf rosettes in autumn, and scarlet gradually suffuses the surrounding spiny leaves. The Cambridge blue form of *Salvia patens* is another speciality; I have taken a lot of cuttings from it this year. A spot is reserved here for *Pennisetum orientale*, one of my favourite grasses; its fluffy mauve heads are like silver bees.

The unheated solarium overlooking this lawn was copied twenty years ago from one at a Georgian house in Worcestershire. I have experimented with many tender plants here. The coral tree (*Erythrina crista-galli*) from Brazil flowered in a meagre fashion outside until I moved it inside three years ago, and it is now quite a different plant, its vigorous stems covered in satiny red flowers. The scarce double-flowered form of the annual nasturtium (*Tropaeolum majus*) is good value and flowers non-stop; being sterile it has to be increased by cuttings each year. *Psoralea*, fifteen feet tall, with ferny foliage and bright blue pea-shaped flowers, is good in early summer.

Streptosolen jamesonii is still *in situ* in the solarium but has proved too rampant: it flowers on the previous year's wood, so it cannot be pruned without losing a year's flower. I like to use the solarium as a sitting room and cannot accommodate plants that are going to take over. For this

OPPOSITE The lily-pool garden, paved with stone from the farm walls and planted with shrubs and alpines in raised beds. Flanking the semi-circular steps are ancient *Viburnum carlesii*.

RIGHT *Magnolia liliiflora* 'Nigra' against a background of flowering quince, *Chaenomeles* 'Phylis Moore'.

BELOW *Myosotidium hortensia* – the giant forget-me-not from the Chatham Islands: it is a difficult plant to grow and consequently a rare one, but the tender care it receives here has produced magnificent results.

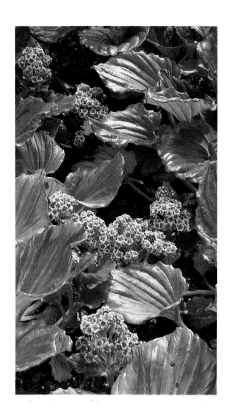

reason I have discarded, in spite of their beauty, an enormous mimosa, *Buddleja madagascariensis* and *Dendromecon rigida*. They all grew so well that there was hardly room for me.

A flight of semicircular stone steps descends from the solarium lawn to the lily pool garden. Once the windbreaks were established, a formal pool was sunk, with its sides and surrounding terrace built of stone from the old farm walls. Following the rectangular shape of the pool are two tiers of raised beds, providing suitable homes, in sun or shade, for choice small shrubs and alpines. Pairs of standard *Viburnum carlesii*, gnarled with age, flank the pool steps.

Hardy orchids, *Sanguinaria canadensis* 'Flore Pleno' (double bloodroot), a fifteen-year-old *Daphne retusa* and a still-flourishing *Salix* 'Boydii' of twenty-five summers are among the plants growing here. *Prunus prostrata*, from the

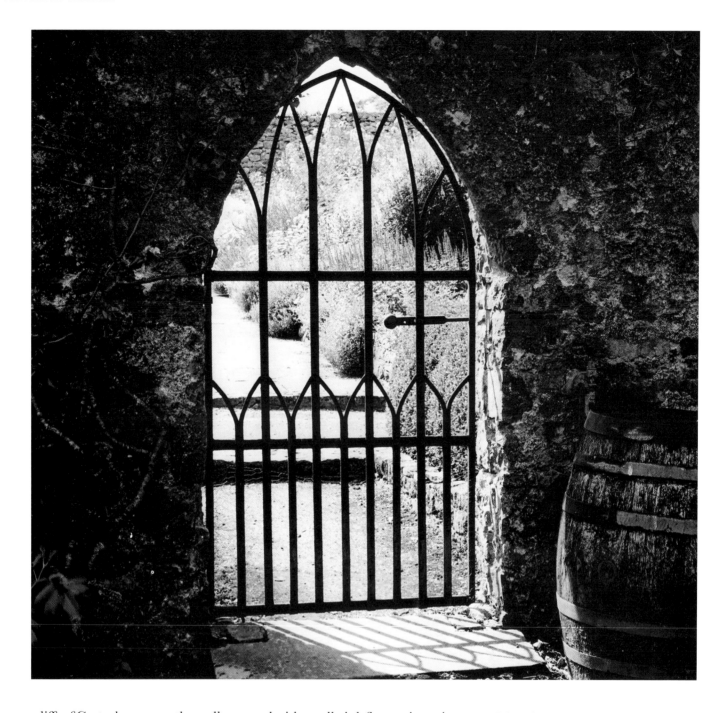

cliffs of Crete, leans over the wall, covered with small pink flowers in spring. This site is ideal for *Tropaeolum polyphyllum*: it can fling its trailing stems around at will to display properly the lemon-gold flowers above a carpet of grey leaves. The pearl-grey flowers of an *Agapanthus* that came from the English plantsman Maurice Mason in Norfolk, and the October-flowering *Hosta tardiflora*, a neat plant with specially large lilac flowers, are among the delights of autumn. Every day of the year is brightened by a silver patch of *Celmisia semicordata*, with a bonus of large white daisies in early summer. Following a hot summer, *Colquhounia coccinea* var. *vestita* flowers well in a warm border nearby.

In an exclusive corner of the lily pool garden resides my only claim to fame, a prospering colony of the Chatham Island forget-me-not, *Myoso-*

Wrought-iron gates at each end of the herbaceous garden are set into the lichen-covered stone walls.

tidium hortensia, sheltered by rhododendrons, tree heaths and a wall. Twenty-five years ago I dug a hole in the field and filled it with peat, and in this home the beautiful forget-me-not has never looked back; it seeds freely every year. The brilliant azure trusses of bloom are reflected in the shining, deeply veined leaves. In the Chatham Islands, New Zealand, it lives on the seashore; here it is not entirely hardy, so it receives an annual mulch of seaweed and is protected by a polythene tent each winter. Nothing is too good for this aristocrat in the world of plants. *Telopea truncata*, a Tasmanian member of the Proteaceae, is allowed to share this favoured spot and generously rewards me with its scarlet flowers.

Between the house and the walled garden is an informal area of woodland. Winding paths wander in dappled light towards the denser shade, where there is a stand of *Cardiocrinum giganteum*, a giant white lily from the Himalayas, and the fragrant, aptly named *Rhododendron* 'Loderi Venus'. Many plants enjoy these conditions, including two excellent *Eucryphia*, *E.* × *intermedia* and *E.* × *nymansensis* 'Mount Usher', *Berberis temolaica*, with leaves of duck-egg blue, *Stewartia pseudocamellia* and a thirty-foot *Cercidiphyllum japonicum* that colours magnificently in autumn. Here grows *Mahonia lomariifolia*, although it might not be recognized as such by connoisseurs: the flowers are at eye and nose level. Nancy Connell, a friend and good gardener, alas now dead, had the idea of tying down the young branches to prevent its normally gawky habit. I copied her: new shoots emerged along the stem and it is now a well-furnished shrub. Underplantings range from *Paeonia obovata* 'Alba' to ferns, willow gentians, bulbs and grasses. I am mad about *Arundo donax*, a lofty reed from the Mediterranean with blue-grey foliage; I can't wait for it to increase.

A gate in an archway opens from the woodland garden on to a wide Liscannor stone walk that divides a pair of raised herbaceous borders. I believe in plenty of farmyard manure at planting time and, for choice, prefer plants that do not require staking. When support is necessary, I like the old-fashioned method of using twiggy beech branches, laboriously cut and sharpened. They are quickly disguised as the foliage grows, and the border looks much prettier than if canes are used. The border, planned for midsummer flowering, is probably at its peak at delphinium time. However, to brighten the days of late summer and autumn there are large groups of blue *Aconitum* 'Arendsii', *Eupatorium purpureum* 'Atropurpureum', much beloved of butterflies, and *Dahlia* 'Bishop of Landaff', with crimson foliage and scarlet flowers.

I have an insatiable appetite for plants: once I get the idea that I want a particular species or variety I cannot rest until it is mine. Often I find that I have placed these hard-won specimens in unsuitable sites. To this day I persist in moving shrubs to what I think, rightly or wrongly, are more favourable positions. Despite repeated admonitions from a friend that I am mad, and that the plant in question won't move, the fact remains that I have few deaths and am usually pleased with the results. I have transplanted *Magnolia campbellii* 'Charles Raffill' no fewer than three times; it has never looked better!

GLIN CASTLE
COUNTY LIMERICK

Madam FitzGerald

OPPOSITE Bluebells and wild garlic carpet the grass under an ancient moss-clad oak tree and blend delicately with the pink of a Japanese maple.

LEFT Lilies and pelargoniums in pots on the terrace. Clinging to the castle walls are wisteria and the rose 'Félicité Perpétue'.

OVERLEAF, ABOVE From a pair of clipped bay trees near the house a path runs the length of the main lawn and culminates in the beautiful *Parrotia persica* planted by Veronica Villiers.

OVERLEAF, BELOW Glin Castle, with the River Shannon in the background. A *Pinus radiata* stands beside the house, and in the foreground are the creamy-white blossoms of *Cornus capitata*.

The garden of Glin Castle in County Limerick is extraordinarily beautiful and yet I feel sure it is not a fine garden. It seems to me to be more of a field cut neatly and circumspectly into a lawn or two, with a little hill that is covered in daffodils in the spring, and some primeval oaks that drench you with their leafy arms as you pass. It is a garden that acknowledges its castle first and foremost, while this battlemented toy fort, preoccupied with its own importance, accepts the homage too carelessly to repay the compliment. Many of its windows treacherously look out over the Shannon estuary or else yearningly, like the rest of us, away down the avenue towards the chimneys and steeple of the village, with an occasional haughty glance down at the croquet lawn and crab apple trees below. The crab apples were planted forty years ago, and for most of the year give the impression of being thickly covered in grey feathery fungus, until they burst into the most unseemly fertility every summer.

A stream, with all the unconscious beauty of a teenager, ambles down one side of the garden, confining between its banks the waters of at least a dozen country springs that have rushed out of the ground further up the hill. Rebelliously confined together, they flow out of the garden and under the last great field in front of the castle before they reach the river.

In the centre of the lawn stands a sundial whose face was made in Limerick in 1765; it records, when possible, the passage of the watery County Limerick sunshine through to the pearly glare of the long midsummer evenings. The sundial stands in what is intended to be a weed-free slate-flagged terrace, and every summer I guiltily transplant flowery wedges of thrift from the cliffs of County Clare, persuading them to re-settle. Surprisingly, they flourish in this alien atmosphere alongside many different thymes, rockroses, pinks and mossy saxifrages, all sheltered from the blistering winds by the friendly gruffness of a circular clipped yew hedge. The lawn is mown in flowing green ribbons, which observe a generous curve round the hedge and continue to the next shaven verge, where two lichen-encrusted urns serve as poignant reminders of their original lakeside home at Belvedere in County Westmeath.

The right-hand side of the garden is a wild delight of magnolias and cherry blossom in spring, with yuccas, myrtles and deep blue hydrangeas flowering for the rest of the year. Tree ferns from Derreen in County Kerry have sent their nervous tender roots into the sodden earth of their first summer at Glin, shrinking faintly away from the monstrous, prickly *Gunnera manicata* nearby. 'Such giant rhubarb', whisper our visitors in awe. The large leaves of the *Gunnera* do indeed resemble their kitchen garden 'cousin', of which we usually have a glut, so that it is easy to foster the illusion that they are one and the same plant by producing quantities of rhubarb sorbet, and maybe one day even a rhubarb soup!

The faint and languorous scent of the *Drimys winteri* drifts over the hill, and the crinodendrons shake their crimson bells in disapprobation at the maidenhair tree, from which the children and I lower our gaze in pagan silence as we pass. The earliest flowering rhododendron shows a pink cheek on the top of the hill around New Year's Day, and in the spring the grass is smudged with bluebells.

To begin with I wanted to smother the walls of the castle in climbing plants but was not allowed ivy, which threatens the fabric, and so found instead the adorable schizophrenic *Ribes speciosum*, with brilliant red prickles on a green stalk and fuchsia flowers hanging next to gooseberry leaves. Wisteria has become tangled in the rose 'Félicité Perpétue' and one wall turns completely blue when the *Ceanothus* flowers in June. Two bay trees, which started life as standard pom-poms before the last war, have grown and been cut into great domed bells at the top of the path, and next to them a vast *Pinus radiata* soughs in the wind.

The garden was laid out when the castle was built, in 1790, but had fallen into disrepair when Lady Rachel Wyndham-Quin married my husband's grandfather, the twenty-seventh Knight of Glin, in 1897. She moved to Glin from nearby Adare Manor and immediately planted the daffodil hill with daffodil bulbs which still flourish today, and which she had imported from her friends the Dorrien-Smiths on Tresco in the Isles of Scilly. Her violets, grown in an area behind the kitchen garden known as 'the violet ground', are said to have been carefully packed in boxes, and transported by donkey cart and train, to be sold at Moyses Stevens in London. No inconsiderable journey even today! My own mother-in-law, Veronica Villiers, who married my husband's father, the twenty-eighth Knight of Glin, in 1929, cut back the brambles which had again encroached, and executed the Edwardian pampas grass on the lawn before planting all the ravishing trees and shrubs that bring us such pleasure today. *Sophora tetraptera* stands on a carpet of its golden pollen, and *Magnolia campbellii* wastes its pink, dove-like buds on the bitterest winds of March. Veronica built a swooping urn-topped wall to keep back the hill, and brilliantly provided as a centrepiece a *Parrotia persica*, whose flowing habit and red leaves cheer the autumns of our days. Great beeches and limes protect and shelter us. Trees seem to grow almost as tall here as in a rain forest.

On the other side of a grey stone wall stands a huge and noble kitchen garden where fig trees, wineberries (*Rubus phoenicolasius*), pears and clematis line the walls, and small sweet black grapes grow in the greenhouse. A headless marble Ariadne is chained to her rock in a newly-built rustic temple, and acres of vegetables and herbs are edged by cascading sweet peas and a cutting border for the house. The hens live in a gothic hen house and a tennis court is completely hidden among the apple trees. Tom Wall, our gardener, combines an angelic temperament with keeping the garden in immaculate trim. Arthur Shackleton comes to advise once a season.

Why is the garden so beautiful? Why, when the River Shannon and the sky are blue, and a hitherto green and sober camellia decides to burst into flower, does one shudder with awe and bliss? Nature and formality are combined with such subtle sensitivity that there is not a clumsy or pretentious note. To me the garden will always be a lovely mystery.

Olda Fitzgerald

HILLMOUNT
COUNTY ANTRIM

Mrs John Frazer

Fifteen years ago we moved to my husband's family home, an eighteenth-century house with a large formal garden some distance away and separated from it by trees and dense shrubberies. It was neither possible nor desirable to continue the upkeep of such a labour-intensive garden as it then was, with herbaceous borders, beds edged with clipped box and extensive fruit and vegetable grounds. We decided to scrap it all and start afresh.

The front of the house faces east. It had a lovely view looking over a ha-ha to a stream and a pond covering about an acre. This was surrounded by a dense ring of laurel and rhododendron, and contained two islands and great clumps of white water lilies. In the distance a wood of beech, oak and Scots pine had been planted. It is known that the pond was excavated in the eighteenth century to make a reservoir for the linen bleach works with which the house has always been associated. Although all looked dark and gloomy, I believed that the combination of water and trees had possibilities, and it was here that I decided my new garden should be laid out, not only to satisfy my own creative feelings but also to enhance the setting of the old house itself, which is much loved by all my family.

We started work in the woodland on the far side of the pond, clearing the undergrowth, draining and digging the heavy clay soil. Now, after years of adding leafmould, compost and grit, the blue poppies and candelabra primulas seed themselves among the rhododendrons. Our annual rainfall is approximately forty inches, but we suffer from crippling May frosts and occasionally the poppies have been blackened just before our 'open garden' day. Other plants grow well here: *Dicentra macrantha*, *Ranzania japonica*, *Uvularia grandiflora*, *Ourisia macrophylla* and *Trollius* all like the cool, damp conditions.

Next, Tommy (a retired bus-driver) and I tackled the pond banks. It was a frightful job cutting and digging out *Rhododendron ponticum* and laurel stumps. We lowered the water by means of a sluice gate, and paddled about in gumboots facing the pond margins with courses of stones. This

done, we could fill behind the stones and create a border round the pond approximately three feet wide, together with a gravel path. Now we could walk on clean ground, and planting began.

On the most exposed side of the pond I put in first daffodils and then hostas and astilbes. This scheme has proved surprisingly effective and labour-saving, as it requires only two weedings in the early part of the season before the foliage covers the ground.

Elsewhere shrubs – *Cornus alba*, *Weigela florida* 'Foliis Purpureis', *Salix lanata*, *Viburnum opulus* 'Xanthocarpum', *Potentilla* 'Daydawn' and 'Red Ace' – make a framework which not only pleases the eye in winter but also provides a setting for many large clumps of perennial plants that give

ABOVE Golden globe flowers, hostas and irises, azaleas and fans of *Cotoneaster horizontalis* border the lake and the islands.

OPPOSITE Azaleas in shades of pink, mauve and crimson, highlighted with white, fringe the water and blend with peonies and a *Philadelphus* in the background.

PREVIOUS PAGE A wooden bridge leads to the islands in the lake and carries the eye on to the creeper-covered Georgian house beyond.

colour throughout the flowering season. In spring the appearance of the white spathes of *Lysichitum camtschatcense* is thrilling; they are followed by many other moisture-loving plants, including *Iris sibirica*, *Rodgersia pinnata* 'Superba' and *Euphorbia polychroma*. As I write, in late autumn after a wet summer, phlox, *Cimicifuga ramosa* 'Atropurpurea', *Hemerocallis*, *Lobelia tupa* and *Gentiana asclepiadea* are all flowering well. I do not grow any plant that requires staking, and I find it important to choose plants which associate well together and with their background. In other words, all must look as natural as possible.

The bramble-covered islands were cleared after our two sons had been persuaded to make, from old telephone posts and split railway sleepers, a bridge across the pond to them. Although not quite in the Japanese style, it carries a wheelbarrow and also many visitors, who seem to find the rather secret island gardens exciting. I discovered that it was difficult to plant the larger island effectively, despite much advice from friends. What looked right on the ground seemed wrong when viewed from the house. After many mistakes, *Cotoneaster horizontalis* and *Bergenia* 'Ballawley' (a hybrid raised at Ballawley Park, Dublin) were planted round the perimeter. The fans of the cotoneaster spread out over the water and give a splendid show of colour in the autumn. Behind is an *Acer griseum* and small shrubs with colourful foliage, groups of *Agapanthus* and autumn crocus (*Colchicum*). The smaller island accommodates a scree garden.

When we came here we pulled down the back of the house – a Victorian addition – and enlarged the area left vacant by cutting down a plantation of thirty beech trees. This provided room to make a small but productive vegetable garden close to the house. This is very handy for the 'cook' who resents spending too much time in the kitchen when she could be weeding. The vegetable garden is getting smaller and smaller as the number of raised beds, housing my expanding collection of alpine plants, increases. Many of these have been grown from seed.

When autumn comes and the leaves fall from the beech trees there is nothing my husband and I like better than raking and making bonfires. This is a do-it-yourself garden and we both love it.

Betty Frazer.

OLD MILL HOUSE
COUNTY DOWN

Mrs Henry Garner

Old Mill House and its garden have experienced many changes. Originally there was a Scutch Mill on the site. To scutch is to break the outer skin of the flax stalk. Long ago the stalk was beaten by hand, but by the time the Mill was built, probably more than two hundred years ago, it was scutched by wooden beaters driven by water power. The Mill was burnt down in 1850, leaving the barn, stables and manager's house. The Mill itself stood where the garden is now, and plants which do not like lime are not happy there, owing to the old mortar rubble.

When my parents married they came to live here, in what used to be the manager's house, and my mother started her garden. It was long and narrow, running the length of the house and barn, with a path down the middle flagged with Scrabo stone taken from the house floors. The borders on each side of the path were full of perennials, sweet sultan, daisies, columbines, peonies and lots of delphiniums. Near the edges of the beds were pansies, the old pink 'Mrs Sinkins' and London pride. My mother was ahead of her time, for annual planting was then the fashion. She bought her plants from Kelway and Son, in Somerset, famous for their peonies and delphiniums. After eighty years or more some of these plants still flower for me.

My first plot was in the big walled garden, where I grew primroses collected from the hedge banks, and slips of plants obtained from the gardener. I was always good at growing these bits and pieces. Then came the First World War. My parents decided to grow extra vegetables in the field in front of the house. After the war, the field was laid out as a tennis court and the rest as a flower garden. The garden now occupies less than an acre and is encircled by a little roadway leading to the yard. The house and garden are on a hillside, from where at one time there was a good view of Belfast Lough, only a few miles away. However, the trees planted to protect the garden from the north wind have flourished and the view is there no longer. The seagulls still seem to find us interesting, for they wheel over the garden constantly keeping a watchful eye on our activities.

The site of the tennis court is naturally level, and from it the land begins to fall away quite steeply in two terraces. Below them is a paved area with three small ponds, or rather pools – one is the abandoned bath (now disguised) from a nearby house – containing pink and white water lilies, and there are *Iris kaempferi* at the sides. The larger pool has a white water lily planted by my mother, which is far too large for the pool and keeps trying to climb out.

I have kept to the general design of the garden I inherited, but have changed its appearance. A big privet hedge has gone, and small trees take its place: *Caragana arborescens* 'Lorbergii', *Liquidambar styraciflua*, *Sorbus*

ABOVE Red-hot pokers against the old brick arches of the mill.

PREVIOUS PAGE Coniferous and deciduous trees, shrubs and perennials: *Prunus subhirtella* 'Autumnalis', *Abies koreana* and *Sorbus* provide a background for a carpet of bronze rock roses and pinks.

'Joseph Rock', *Sorbus sargentiana*, *Sophora tetraptera*, and a number of others. There are also shrubs: *Sambucus racemosa* 'Plumosa Aurea', *Syringa × persica*, S. 'Primrose', *S. microphylla*, and *Philadelphus coronarius*, all of them laced with *Rosa filipes* 'Kiftsgate' and *Rosa moyesii* to make a solid hedge between the garden and the little road. This hides the long roof of the old outbuildings where the carts belonging to the Mill were kept.

The road running round the garden leads into a large stone-walled yard. Here there are beds of *Kniphofia praecox*, bergenias and lacecap hydrangeas, with various old roses filling the corners. I am fortunate in still having part of the old Scrabo stone wall on the north side of the lawn, which was formerly the tennis court. It has a little peephole through which the watchman could see the entrance to the Mill. Nearby are stone-capped brick piers, which still carry the iron supports for the big wooden gates leading to the Mill. In the border below the wall I grow *Buddleja colvilei*, *Berberidopsis corallina*, *Cestrum* 'Newellii', *C. parqui*, *Magnolia grandiflora* 'Ferruginea', and a golden yellow honeysuckle which climbs through *Azara microphylla* 'Variegata'.

Near the house is a tall *Nothofagus dombeyi* and a long bed of heathers and old-fashioned pinks, with small bulbs edging the lawn in the spring. In this bed is a very old *Picea abies* 'Clanbrassilliana', a low prickly green mound of unknown age. To introduce variety in the height of the plants I have planted *Abies koreana* and a tall pillar-like juniper, and also two roses, *Rosa macrophylla* and *R. ecae*, both grown from seed collected in Nepal. At the end of this bed is *Cotoneaster salicifolius*, covered with flowers in summer and in winter a mass of red berries which the birds do not eat.

There is a wide, paved path between the heathers and the next border, though it can hardly be called a path now, for plants seem to like growing on it. This border has two principal trees, *Amelanchier canadensis* and *Prunus subhirtella* 'Autumnalis', with charming pinky-white flowers lasting from autumn well past the spring. Beside this path is an elder, *Sambucus nigra* 'Guincho Purple', its leaves a deep brown. This colouring shows off the large cream flowers of the rose 'Nevada'. Underneath all this are cranesbills, Japanese anemones, the peach rose 'Cornelia' and *Cornus alba* 'Elegantissima', with brilliant red stems in winter. The path leads back to the house, which itself shelters numerous climbers that cause considerable trouble by getting under the slates on the roof. *Hydrangea petiolaris* is the worst culprit.

On the first of the terraces, which is fortunately the widest, is *Acer palmatum* 'Dissectum', but it is getting too large for its site here. In autumn it colours like a flame. To compete with it, on the opposite side of the path, is the scarlet oak (*Quercus coccinea*).

Down some steps, on the lower terrace, a large rose 'Buff Beauty' scents the air. There are numerous old roses here whose names I do not know, as well as *Syringa microphylla* 'Superba', *Drimys winteri* and *Stachyurus praecox*, and above them all a *Hoheria lyallii*, with its mass of cherry-like flowers. All these plants came from the Slieve Donard Nursery. Further steps lead down to the ponds, where *Luma apiculata*, *Myrtus communis*, *Abutilon × suntense*, *Mahonia lomariifolia* and *Rosa chinensis* 'Mutabilis' flourish. Silver birch trees, gathered from the nearby railway bank, stand above this gently sloping area. With our long hours of northern light in midsummer there is practically no night – and it is lovely to be in the garden late, when colours are enhanced and scents entrancing.

Eighteen months ago a terrible gale blew down a number of our best

Margaret Garner gathering rose-pink clusters of the semi-evergreen *Buddleja colvilei* – the largest-flowered species of butterfly bush.

ABOVE A mixed shrub and flower border in front of Old Mill House, with a columnar juniper as its centrepiece. *Hydrangea petiolaris* clings to the wall in the background.

OPPOSITE The cream flowers of *Sambucus nigra* 'Guincho Purple' and the rose 'Nevada' overhang a garden seat, and a magnificent scarlet poppy displays the velvet-black markings within the flower.

trees, including a large and very old beech tree that sheltered the garden from the east wind. It is sadly missed but its demise has made a place for a new bed. Plants and shrubs that had only just survived under the beech are now thriving. I have planted two young trees here – *Betula* 'Jermyns' and *B. utilis* – as a step towards providing some shelter.

Over the years I have lost many plants, but I have also acquired many. I keep a book in which I enter any plants I buy or am given. Cuttings are not recorded, for I am never certain if they have survived. To make up for failures, there are the plants which need no care, such as hellebores, hostas, sheets of snowdrops, and valerian in red, white and two shades of pink, which grows in all our walls and will always be with us.

Margaret AK Garner

DARGLE COTTAGE
COUNTY WICKLOW

The Hon. Lady Goulding

'One day', said my husband Basil, 'I'll make a garden.' He was flat on his back at the time, recovering from an injury, and his mother had given him some books on gardening to occupy his mind.

He was not one to do things by halves. In 1947, when we were looking for a house, friends living in Enniskerry, near Bray, County Wicklow, told us that they had found just the place. It was Dargle Cottage, a tiny house with a small, overgrown cabbage patch, about a mile and a half east of Enniskerry and the same distance from the sea. I was away when Basil went to look at it, but the moment he saw the place he bought it.

Its chief glory is the Dargle Glen, a spectacularly steep and densely wooded gorge, gouged out by a glacier thousands of years ago, and deepened by the River Dargle as it noisily carves its way to the sea. In most places the river has had little difficulty in cutting a path through soft, metamorphosed sandstone and slate. Elsewhere it has had to make its way round the harder quartzite outcrops which force it to twist and turn and gurgle as it tumbles busily seawards. The sound of water is everywhere in the Dargle Glen, murmuring, hissing, thundering down steep but short-lived waterfalls and foaming rapids. When I first visited our new home I knew at once that Basil had chosen the right place.

But where were we to put the garden? The banks of the gorge, almost vertical in places, were covered in oak, ash, pine and hazel. A dense undergrowth of brambles and nettles had established itself where even the trees could not gain a foothold. Basil was not in the least deterred by these obstacles. He had decided there would be a garden, and a garden there would be. And he considered it would be incomplete unless it occupied both sides of the river, so he bought the land opposite (originally owned by Lord Monck of Charleville) from the Kilcroney Golf Club. While the purchase was being negotiated, the hard work of clearing the undergrowth and levelling the ground into terraces began. These were planted with trees, shrubs and many roses.

The next problem was how to cross the gorge, from one side of the garden

A view across the glen showing one of the tubular modern sculptures acquired by Basil Goulding.

to the other. Basil commissioned a design for a bridge, but the plans took so long to draw up that in the end he designed it himself and, with a little help, built it. At the time we had some doubts about how long the bridge would stand before collapsing into the gorge, but that was thirty years ago and it is still in daily use.

Willie Kerrigan, our head gardener, and a couple of local men helped to plant the first part of the garden on the far side of the bridge. Basil cleared the wilderness and planted a water garden with ferns, *Gunnera manicata*, *Lysichitum americanum* and a variety of shrubs that thrive in damp soil. The centrepiece of the water garden was a one-room cedar cottage, bought from the Golf Club. There was also a large rhododendron, but Basil did not much care for it; he called it 'blowsy'.

He meticulously mapped and documented every plant. This was just as well, because if he decided that a particular shrub did not look right or was not thriving in its chosen position, he would suddenly move it. Sometimes large bushes would disappear overnight from one part of the garden and turn up in another. The new position would then be marked on the map. Many of the local people told us that not much would survive in the Dargle Glen, as it is a notorious frost pocket. We have taken much delight in proving them wrong again and again.

Basil's impatience that each plant should do well and look right was offset by a cheerful resignation when there was nothing he could do to hurry Nature along. For instance, one of the first trees to be planted was *Magnolia campbellii* – a considerable act of faith because he knew it would not bloom for twenty years. We held a party to celebrate when it eventually produced its giant pink tulips. There is also a fine specimen of *Magnolia campbellii* var. *mollicomata*, which flowers at a younger age. Varieties of *Sorbus* (including *S. matsumarana*), a *Davidia involucrata* and a *Catalpa* grow here too, and there are many hollies which Basil collected over the years, among them the true *Ilex*, 'Silver Queen', 'Pyramidalis' and 'Argentea Marginata'. Near the house he planted the great white cherry, *Prunus* 'Tai Haku', *Embothrium coccineum* 'Norquinco' and *Eucryphia glutinosa*.

From 1947 until Basil's death in January 1982, the garden grew in more senses than one. I often used to say that it was quite large enough, but he energetically carried on driving back the wilderness and planting anew. Over the years Dr Neil Murray, a close friend and an eminent horticulturist, came to visit him, discuss the garden and help him with the planting. Our present head gardener, Noel Keogh, who came to us at the age of seventeen, has been a tower of strength for thirty years. Once in a while Noel and Basil would disagree on policy. Basil, for instance, liked the giant hogweed (*Heracleum mantegazzianum*) which grows on the river banks, but Noel did not. One day when Basil wasn't looking, Noel cut it down. The last bit of land which they reclaimed was planted with *Eucalyptus coccifera*, *Taxodium distichum*, *Berberis calliantha*, maples and *Rhododendron* species.

Growing beside the avenue is a good specimen of the weeping blue cedar, *Cedrus atlantica* 'Pendula'. It used to be even finer, but unfortunately a passing van removed one of its branches, which had formed an arch over the avenue.

The natural formation of Dargle Glen is strange enough in itself, but Basil added his own touches, saying, 'Nature sometimes needs a rap over the knuckles.' Visitors to the garden almost always comment on the strange pieces of tubular modern sculpture that he bought and placed in prominent positions. Nature, however, has got her own back: teazels have

The Dargle River has carved its way through sandstone and slate and winds a more meandering course around outcrops of quartzite to its mouth near Bray, south of Dublin.

grown up handsomely round an aluminium pillar – which Basil and I agreed is an improvement.

Flower arranging gave him further scope for gentle eccentricity. He had a habit of including at least one foreign object in his arrangement of flowers; one composition featured a plastic roll of 8 mm film. His off-beat approach was not confined to sculpture and flower arranging. Architecture was another hobby, and in the upper part of the garden he and Ronnie Tallon, an architect, built a steel-framed, wooden summerhouse which was cantilevered so that three-fifths of it protrudes, unsupported, over the gorge and river 100 feet below. This spectacular and gravity defying building, like the bridge, looks as though it ought to fall down at any moment. However, it has been used not only as an ideal spot for parties but also as a successful restaurant.

High above the river stands a large plant of the Australian tree fern *Dicksonia antarctica*, one of the plants that should not grow in our frost pocket, but so far it has survived many hard winters. This fern looks down on the water garden and the bridge. Growing nearby, among the rocks and overhanging the river, is *Hydrangea villosa*, its mauve lacecaps almost touching the water.

Basil wrote many articles about gardening, usually in a humorous vein,

OPPOSITE, ABOVE The valley of the Dargle, planted with a superb collection of trees that provide interest and a rich variety of colour and texture throughout the year.

OPPOSITE, BELOW Wisteria on the bridge that spans the gorge.

and his final masterpiece was a monograph, *Twelve Elegant Fallacies for Woodland Gardens*. Here is part of his comment on Fallacy No. 11:

Pruning is a mystique set up and sanctificated by gardeners, much as pebble-dashing is by plasterers or stippling by painters. You have only got to have a bash at any of these presumptions to unfrock them.

I am no gardener myself. Perhaps it is just as well, or Basil and I might have disagreed over the garden. As it is, I continue to enjoy what he created as much as I enjoyed the making of it. Thirty-five years of hard work, and the dedication and inspiration of a singular mind, have turned a little-known beauty spot into one of the great heritage gardens of Ireland.

Editorial note: In January 1985 the garden, together with the house and restaurant, was sold to Mr Tony Ryan.

Valerie Goulding

PRIMROSE HILL
COUNTY DUBLIN

Mrs Cicely Hall

When we bought Primrose Hill in the 1950s the house needed a lot of repair, so it was more with a feeling of exhaustion than enthusiasm that we turned our attention to the garden. The debris left by the building work, as well as the dangerous trees that had to be felled, caused quite a problem.

The garden then consisted of a lawn with rose beds, a few flowering shrubs, a small border, a vegetable patch and an orchard of ailing apple trees. The house faces south, across the lawn to a party hedge of elders and brambles. As the garden is small and surrounds the house, we had to

'Primrose Hill specials'.

82

ABOVE Pinks spread out over the stone in front of a border backed by junipers and the silver tiers of a fine dogwood, *Cornus controversa* 'Variegata'.

The tender *Lobelia tupa*. In its native Chile, hummingbirds flit from flower to flower, sipping nectar from the crimson flasks.

83

camouflage the hedge with planting; the elders still flourish in the part over which we have no control. Our neighbour's large beech tree fell three years ago, changing the character of part of the garden and giving us a more open aspect. This was an improvement once we got used to it. As the house stands high, exposed to westerly gales, we planted shelter belts for long term and hedges for short term protection. The land slopes from west to east, and to break the slope we created the effect of a raised bed.

I would like to be able to claim that we planned the garden with method and foresight. We didn't; I can only say that the lawn has got smaller as the garden has gradually encroached. In the process we have uncovered old rubbish heaps and cinder paths that had been grassed over. To add to our problems, the soil is stony and lacks humus.

With makeshift facilities for propagation we achieve a reasonable degree of success for our needs. *Cornus controversa* 'Variegata' – now a handsome twenty-year-old, and *Magnolia wilsonii* (the latter from seed) take pride of place. From the Slieve Donard Nursery we bought one of my favourite plants, *Kniphofia snowdenii* and also *Meconopsis* × *sheldonii* 'Slieve Donard'. This is a tough stayer, having survived and flowered well in the far from ideal conditions of this comparatively hot, dry garden.

We do not succeed with roses; spray as we may it doesn't seem to help, and it becomes boring having to explain away our shortcomings. Fortunately 'Céleste' one of my favourites, seems trouble free; I am also fond of 'De Meaux', which was given to me by a gardening friend whose family originally brought it from France in the 1800s, and had kept it going

Varieties of *Iris, Geranium, Paeonia* and *Penstemon* seen through a filigree screen of *Crambe cordifolia* at Primrose Hill.

from generation to generation. The same friend alerted me to look for a 'little black dahlia' whose loss she mourned, and which we finally tracked down to a specialist nursery in England as *Cosmos atrosanguineus*; it has delighted me ever since.

Aphyllanthes monspeliensis was sold to me as a waterside plant. We planted it beside a very large trough, in which we put a mini water lily, and it certainly looked the part, with its rush-like leaves; we were delighted with its blue flowers among the primulas. It has flourished, increased, survived horrific frosts and gets no sun. A very knowledgeable friend, David Shackleton, pointed out that it comes from southern Italy, and likes hot and dry conditions. I then checked, which I should have done in the first place, and he was of course right – but I haven't moved it.

A planting combination I am particularly pleased with is *Veratrum nigrum* backed by an old-fashioned white phlox, but a totally disastrous planting was a group of the startling orange-red *Tulipa sprengeri* next to a magenta hardy marsh orchid with a shrill pink rockrose lurking nearby. The rockrose has been taken out, but as the tulips and orchids are happy we just have to live with the clash.

I cannot resist self-sown seedlings, although they make the garden look disorderly. Admittedly the *Kniphofia* and herbaceous *Lobelia* seedlings are not all that impressive yet, but I am very flattered that *Fritillaria pontica* has become weed-like in its wish to naturalize.

We still have the double green and old double red auriculas that came from the well-known plantswoman Miss Winifred Wynne, as well as a charming small early double daffodil, which nobody can name. *Viola* 'Jackanapes' and the hen-and-chicken daisy, *Bellis perennis* var. *prolifera*, were given to me when I was about eight years old by Mrs Shaw-Smith of Ballawley for my first garden (I would like to be able to say that I kept them all that time!), and they have remained for me an absolute must ever since.

For interest all the year round we rely on individual plants more than a general effect. An unexpected success came with snowdrops, some of which we brought with us from our previous garden; they then interbred with gay abandon, giving us some interesting 'Primrose Hill specials'. I collect seed haphazardly, and sow it in rows like spring onions. The seedlings flower after three years and we select the best of them, which in their turn have seeded. Each year we re-select, and we now have quite a lot of nice hybrids, with a few we consider to be of special merit. We have had a number of seedlings with two flowers to a stem. Unfortunately the second flower is often misshapen, in which case the plant remains merely a curiosity, and those with two perfect flowers are remarkably unstable, but perhaps we will be lucky one day.

Twenty-seven years on, our shelter belts have done well, the temporary hedges are out, and only one apple tree remains. The soil is still stony, but the humus content is greatly improved. As we haven't striven for any special effects, or specialized in any particular aspect of gardening, there only remains for me to say how lucky we have been in knowing such generous gardeners past and present who have given us many of our choicest plants.

Cicely M. Hall.

GUINCHO
COUNTY DOWN

William Harrison

Guincho is situated nine miles east of Belfast, on the north coast of County Down, 240 feet above sea level, and one mile from the sea. The annual rainfall is about 35 inches, and although the climate is generally mild, 14°F (−10°C) of frost have been experienced during a bad winter, and north and east winds in January and February can do damage to our plants. Its neutral soil and good drainage enables a wide range of species to be grown.

In 1948, when Mr and Mrs Frazer Mackie bought Guincho, a property of sixteen acres, it contained mostly herbaceous and bedding plants – not at all to Mrs Mackie's taste – and she set about creating her own kind of garden. In planting a garden one has to be very discerning, not introducing too much of one thing, or concentrating on colour to the detriment of everything else. Mrs Mackie never lost her head; she made a plantsman's garden, with the emphasis on rarity, and her disciplined and careful selection produced a result that is both decorative and interesting.

She acquired seed from various parts of the world, and mature plants grown from this seed now flourish at Guincho. Plants from the Royal Botanic Garden, Edinburgh, and the Royal Horticultural Society Garden at Wisley, as well as private gardens, found their way here.

The house, which is Portuguese in style, is approached by a short, secluded drive. In front is a large oval bed, planted with hybrid rhododendrons, hydrangeas and pampas grass, backed by a large *Escallonia* hedge. The grassed terrace at the back of the house has square and rectangular beds. Mrs Mackie was particularly fond of shrub roses, so these beds are filled with an interesting collection including 'Fru Dagmar Hastrup', which has a good flower and crimson hips, 'Poulsen's Pink', 'Céleste', which is my favourite, and 'Rosier de l'Ile Bourbon'.

Among the plants that cling to the house is a large specimen of *Sophora tetraptera*, with yellow pea-like flowers – truly a sight to behold in May. Close by, *Puya caerulea* 'Pygmaea' does extremely well, and flowers every year. Another shrub of note is the lemon-scented *Aloysia triphylla*, here almost six feet tall.

In the shrubbery near the house is a fine specimen of the Tasmanian shrub *Acradenia frankliniae*, with dark green trifoliate leaves and clusters of white flowers in May. Another Australian plant is *Banksia marginata*; when in flower this attracts a lot of attention. Several *Olearia* species flourish here, along with the American *Myrica californica* and *M. cerifera*, and *Euonymus lucidus*, its new growth a lovely crimson in the springtime and turning to deep green later in the season.

At the top of the steps to the paved garden are *Rosa omeiensis* var. *pteracantha*, *Corokia macrocarpa* and the attractive *C. × virgata*, with large green leaves, white beneath, and bright orange fruits. Another *Puya*, this one *P. alpestris*, flourishes in this part of the garden. At the bottom of the steps is an attractive, erect-growing honeysuckle, *Lonicera chaetocarpa*, and behind it a fine specimen of *Ribes speciosum*. And in the paved garden itself, surrounded by a low wall, grow *Senecio laxifolius*, *S. monroi* and *Leptospermum humifusum*. Two members of the rose family inhabit the pavement crevices, a large plant of *Dryas × suendermanii* and, from the Andes, *Margyricarpus setosus*. In a sheltered corner is *Arum creticum*. The grey foliage of *Tropaeolum polyphyllum*, topped by beautiful yellow flowers, cascades down the walls. Early spring sees this garden at its best, when all the small bulbs are in flower – *Crocus tommasinianus*, *Chionodoxa luciliae*, *Scilla sibirica*, *Muscari racemosum* – but it is the American *Erythronium* (Mrs Mackie's favourite spring flowers) that are outstanding. One, which she thought very highly of, *E. citrinum* var. *purdyi*, came to her from California from Mr Elmer Purdy. These American relatives of the dog-tooth violet thrive not only in the paved garden but also throughout the borders and woodland. *E. revolutum* and a selection, 'Pink Beauty', are prolific, having seeded profusely in the woods, with a little encouragement. Two others worth mentioning in the collection are *E. californicum*, with mottled leaves and creamy-white flowers, and *E. grandiflorum*, with green leaves and bright yellow flowers.

Turn right along a paved path. Here *Rhododendron lowndesii* flourishes beside the white-berried *Pernettya tasmanica* and two little *Hebe* which came from New Zealand. *Olearia floribunda*, another Tasmanian species, has minute deep green leaves covering its branches, and masses of small white flowers in June; it is slightly tender, but has survived here for ten years. The dwarf *Forsythia viridissima* 'Bronxensis', *Escallonia* 'Iveyi', *Berberis temolaica* and *Phormium tenax* 'Veitchii' also do well here.

Crossing a small rectangular lawn, with banks of *Senecio* 'Sunshine' and the sweet-smelling double gorse, we come to a charming small, circular garden, partly surrounded by a low wall. It contains some unusual trees and shrubs, probably the most outstanding being a native of New Zealand, *Pseudopanax crassifolius*. It came here as a very small plant, and was watched over with great care; it is now around twenty-five feet high. Another tree from the same part of the world is *Hakea saligna*. Alongside is *Myrtus lechleriana*, its copper-coloured leaves reminding one of *Vaccinium ovatum*. The various bottle-brushes and tea trees give a great splash of colour during August. The award-winning purple-leaved elder, *Sambucus nigra* 'Guincho Purple', was found by Mrs Mackie in the wild, near Abertay in Perthshire, Scotland, and at Guincho it is now a well-clothed small tree. She was justly proud of this decorative foliage plant: the pinky-cream fragrant flowers are beautifully shown off by the rich bronze-purple of the leaves that lasts the summer through.

The low wall is covered with masses of *Daboecia cantabrica*, giving colour later in the year. In the small borders are a number of heathers, including a fine *Erica arborea* 'Alpina'. One cannot leave this area without mentioning two more Tasmanian plants: *Trochocarpa thymifolia*, one of the rarest and oldest in the garden – Mrs Mackie acquired it shortly after coming to Guincho – and *Senecio brunonis*, a tree groundsel, with narrow green leaves and yellow flowers.

From the steps of the paved garden we enter an expanse of grass, sloping gently down to open woodland through which a stream meanders. The lawn is the centrepiece of the main plantings – long, wide borders of trees, species and hybrid rhododendrons, shrubs and herbaceous plants. Guincho is, I suppose, known for its trees and shrubs, but it also has a wonderful collection of herbaceous plants, and these borders are colourful throughout spring, summer and autumn. There are large plantings of cranesbills, *Agapanthus*, *Kniphofia* and *Watsonia* (raised by Mrs Mackie from seed sent from South Africa), *Polygonatum*, *Trillium*, *Disporum* and many special herbaceous plants. During the winter *Garrya elliptica*, with its long grey-green catkins, *Hamamelis mollis* and a collection of *Sarcococca*, with small, fragrant flowers, provide pleasure. Hydrangeas abound through these borders: 'Ayesha' (a favourite of mine), a large mass of *Hydrangea rosthornii*, *H. sargentiana* and *H. arborescens* 'Sterilis' and many others.

Before describing the woodland I must mention yet another Tasmanian

ABOVE William Harrison's gardening tools; he oils them every week.

ABOVE RIGHT William Harrison and a large specimen of the hardy evergreen bamboo from China, *Arundinaria murielae*.

PREVIOUS PAGES: ABOVE *Erythronium revolutum* (American trout lily) which has spread over sixty square yards and is one of the rare and beautiful sights to be seen at Guincho in the spring. BELOW Autumn at Guincho: sun lighting drops of rain on the almost bare branches of a maple and a carpet of fallen leaves.

shrub, *Anopterus glandulosa*, which has lovely clear white flowers; *Betula utilis* 'Trinity College' was planted in 1953, propagated by Hillier and Son from a plant in the now destroyed College Botanic Garden in Ballsbridge, Dublin.

The woodland is a lovely place, cool and peaceful and full of interest, with birds, wild plants and a stream, the banks of which are cloaked with masses of ferns and bamboos. *Picea breweriana* and *P. smithiana* grow in a glade, as does the Huon pine of Tasmania, *Dacrydium franklinii*. A large tree of the Chilean hazel, *Gevuina avellana*, inhabits a high bank above the stream, along with maples, *Oxydendrum arboreum* and many other trees giving lovely autumn colour. Other plants of note are four tree ferns, *Dicksonia antarctica* and the Kauri pine, *Agathis australis*.

Large-leaved rhododendrons are a special feature of the woodland. There are fine plants of the Barbatum, Thomsonii, Falconeri, Grande and Fortunei series, along with those incomparable hybrids *Rhododendron* 'Loderi King George' and 'Loderi Venus'.

Mrs Mackie died in October 1979, and Guincho now belongs to Dr and Mrs Meshida. The many people who have visited the garden over the years will be pleased to know that it has not been altered. Dr and Mrs Meshida have been kind in allowing some old friends of Guincho to visit the garden and only last year the Irish Garden Plant Society paid us a visit.*

Mrs Mackie was a very kind lady, a fine and knowledgeable gardener, and a wonderful teacher with great patience. I had the pleasure of being her head gardener for twenty-three years.

William E. Harrison

*Editorial note: On the occasion of this visit William Harrison was made the fourth honorary member of the Irish Garden Plant Society, an honour bestowed on a quiet, unassuming man whose part in creating this great garden should not go unrecorded. Guincho's survival since 1979 is due, in great part, to William Harrison's continued presence there as head gardener.

STRAMORE
COUNTY WEXFORD
Mrs Dorothy Jobling-Purser

I bought Elm Park in Rathfarnham, near Dublin, after my husband's death, and of all the responsibilities I had then, I was most frightened of having to cope with the garden. I was fortunate to be able to get Lanning Roper to help and advise me, and this started a friendship of the greatest pleasure; it was he who taught me the real joy one could derive from gardening. I kept an accurate catalogue of all the plants at Elm Park, where they were planted, who gave them to me and what nurseries they came from (alas, so many of these nurseries are no more). I also had a 'fairy godmother' in Lady Moore, who lived nearby. She used to drive up at the most unexpected times saying, 'I want you to get to know really good plants', and open the boot of her car to reveal the precious things she had brought for my garden. The interest of such a knowledgeable person was most stimulating, as was the wonderful advice I was given by Philip Wood of the Slieve Donard Nursery in Newcastle, County Down.

From Elm Park I restored the overgrown garden at Marble Hill in County Donegal. There was a good greenhouse there with a mist-propagator, and I became completely absorbed in propagating plants. On arrival at Stramore in 1979 I had plenty of decent-sized plants with which to make another garden, and felt proud I had grown them myself.

Stramore, in Bunclody, was bought on impulse. It is a modern, easily run bungalow, situated in a bowl of good farming land that sweeps up to the Blackstairs Mountains and Mount Leinster. An ever-changing atmosphere dominates the whole place. When Lanning and I were discussing what I should do to make a garden, we realized that it must flow naturally into the landscape.

The one-acre site is historically interesting. The house next door, built by Huguenots, has a water mill. Its orchard, enclosed by a dry stone wall completely covered in ivy, was my plot. The first thing I wanted to do was pull off all the ivy, but I soon realized that had I done this there would have been no wall: it was entirely held up by ivy.

At first the soil seemed poor, stony and full of slate (there is an outcrop of

ABOVE A herringbone dry stone wall capped with *Aubrieta* and *Alchemilla mollis*.

LEFT Dorothy Jobling-Purser, apron-clad, gathering roses.

PREVIOUS PAGE The terraced garden at Stramore, looking out to the Blackstairs Mountains. A *Potentilla* (shrubby yellow cinquefoil) and *Alchemilla mollis* (lady's mantle) establish a golden theme in the planting around the stone-flagged upper terrace.

slate at a nearby quarry), but I was quite wrong – it is fertile and well-drained. Specimen trees I planted in the spring of 1980 amazed me by their speed of growth.

I inherited some nice cherry trees, including *Prunus subhirtella* 'Autumn-alis', and several good shrubs beside the house. There is a paved terrace at the front, looking to the hills, with steps down to a second terrace, which is sheltered, private and sunny – much appreciated by sunbathers. At the back of the house is a sun room which I use a great deal as a workroom. To this I added a conservatory a couple of steps lower than the house. A path and sloping flowerbeds, which give me great pleasure in the summer, encircle it.

On the lawn below, we have a small orchard of miniature apple trees. In the spring *Iris histrioides* blooms in the beds beneath them, and snowdrops, crocuses and huge drifts of daffodils carpet the lawn. The daffodils came from Brian Duncan and David Campbell, renowned daffodil breeders in Omagh. I had to plant them in the lawn as there was nowhere else, but so far they have done extraordinarily well. It is a long daffodil season; I find it exciting and am always sad when it is over.

We decided that the most natural treatment for this part of the garden was to make large borders at the foot of the walls, with serpentine margins.

A catalogue of the plants at Elm Park, near Dublin, many of which were used to restore the garden at Marble Hill, Donegal, and to form the basis of Dorothy Jobling-Purser's new garden at Stramore.

We have filled these with flowering trees, shrubs and roses, and with the many interesting plants that have either been given to me by good friends or bought at the suggestion of Lanning. These include *Hacquetia epipactis*, *Hoheria*, *Kirengeshoma palmata*, *Helichrysum lanatum*, *Hydrangea villosa*, *Kolkwitzia*, several *Rodgersia*, *Myosotidium hortensia* and some interesting cultivars of *Phormium* which I brought from New Zealand. Other favourites are peonies, including a fine specimen of *Paeonia mlokosewitschii*, lilies and hostas, of which I have a good collection made over the years, and various hellebores that do well here, especially *Helleborus corsicus*.

Now all the beds are full, and we will have to spend the winter throwing things out. To help me with this I have an enthusiastic gardener two days a week, and my cook-housekeeper who is a tremendous help as a weeder. She now knows all my plants, and only throws out the weeds!

Dorothy Jobling-Purser

ABOVE Stonecrops, pinks and broom crown a wall beneath which catmint, arum and day lilies and hostas flourish.

OPPOSITE A quince overhangs this ivy-clad wall and below it roses, tricolor sage and a purple *Cotinus* give colour.

KILBOGGET
COUNTY DUBLIN
Sidney Maskell

Soon after the Second World War we began to look for a site on which to build a house. At that time I had to commute to Dublin every day and was decidedly more interested in golf than plants, although my wife was a good and experienced gardener. Eventually, in 1948, I came across a two-and-a-half-acre field on the south-western slope of Killiney hill. The view of the Dublin and Wicklow Mountains was spectacular, but the real attraction was the proximity to Killiney golf course. The site, some distance from the main road, was ideal – rectangular in shape and sloping considerably to the south-west – but bare of vegetation, except grass. The building of the house and the making of the garden began in 1949. I soon became hooked on gardening, and have hardly put a foot on the golf course since.

It was not long before we realized that the features of the site created a micro-climate favourable to the cultivation of half-hardy trees and shrubs. This fact has become more and more evident as time has passed and satisfactory shelter has been provided.

Tests on the soil revealed a pH of 7, which was a good start, but a thin layer of heavy clay over granite was not promising. Rainfall here is about thirty-three inches a year and the soil dries out quickly: there have been as many deaths from drought as from frost. Nevertheless, most plants have done well and growth has been generally good.

How were we to lay out the garden? Advice, both professional and amateur, was freely given: 'Plant rows of poplars as a windbreak'; 'Get a contractor to terrace the garden'; 'Break it up into compartments by planting lots of hedges'. However, none of these ideas seemed appropriate. Surely, with such a splendid distant outlook, and the view of the tower of the nearby church in the centre of the lower boundary, a different approach was called for. Whatever method was adopted, it was essential to preserve the view and to try and make the garden blend into the countryside.

We read not a few books and Michael Haworth-Booth came up with a possible solution in his fine book *The Flowering Shrub Garden*: he advocated and find suitable places in which to plant them. There have been many mistakes – and many successes. Probably the main fault has been to put in too much and we are now paying for it. Plants have been lost through overcrowding; small ones have been swallowed up; a *Griselinia* hedge became too big; we have allowed the lawn to become infested with weeds; we have planted too many *Prunus* and we have accepted gifts of undesirable plants!

Some successes have been the result of deliberate planting, others are pure accidents. We believe the layout and design are successful, and that we have done the right thing in taking advantage of the mild climate. We now have a notable collection of unusual plants from all over the world. They are not necessarily the best garden plants, but all of them are interesting and many are very decorative.

We have enjoyed creating the garden and, until recently, maintaining it ourselves. Maintenance is becoming more difficult – and the rabbits and vine weevils are no help. Visitors have praised it and the late Lanning Roper, when he wrote about it in *Country Life*, said it was 'a plantsman's garden come true'.

planting with the idea of a glade in mind. This was at least worth trying. So trees and shrubs were planted around the perimeter of the site, bordering an open expanse of grass which leads from the house to the lower boundary. Specimen trees were planted in the lawn, and large island beds formed in the more sheltered lower areas. A terrace the full length of the house was vital: one must have a level area for seats in which to relax and enjoy the view and admire the garden. The terrace, paved with stone flags but with pockets for plants, has been most successful.

The walls of the house provide a good home for a number of not-so-hardy plants such as *Fremontodendron* 'California Glory', *Cestrum* 'Newellii', *Jasminum polyanthum*, a couple of *Puya*, *Cantua buxifolia*, *Vallea stipularis* 'Pyrifolia', *Cassia corymbosa*, *Psoralea pinnata* and *Myrsine africana*. On the lower terrace flourishing plants include *Moltkia petraea*, *Prostanthera*, *Mimulus* and *Fascicularia*. The climbing golden hop with that awful name, *Humulus lupulus* 'Aureus', looks well climbing over *Cotoneaster horizontalis*. Specimen trees on the lawn range from a much admired *Abies koreana* to *Picea omorika*, *Picea likiangensis* and a large specimen of *Cornus capitata* that never fails to flower. Other fine plants include *Sorbus sargentiana*, *Lomatia furruginea*, *Luma apiculata* and *Myrtus lechleriana*, *Thuja koraiensis* and a cedar or two.

The shelter belt is made up of a mixed bag: *Prunus*, *Pittosporum*, *Hoheria*, maples, several conifers and various other trees. The perimeter borders and island beds contain a collection of trees, shrubs, herbaceous plants and bulbs. There are several magnolias, of which *Magnolia* × *watsonii* and *M. salicifolia* are favourites. Of the *Eucryphia* genus, *E. lucida* is a beauty, but pride of place must go to *E. cordifolia*. There are rhododendrons galore, but I now agree with the late Edward Walpole of Mount Usher that one can plant too many. In our experience, plants of the Maddenii series are hardier than is normally expected. We are lucky to have good forms of *Rhododendron augustinii*, *R. thomsonii*, *R. davidsonianum*, *R. yunnanense* and the magnificent *R. megacalyx*.

Among herbaceous plants we admire and grow are *Rodgersia*, *Myosotidium hortensia*, *Veratrum* and *Watsonia*. We are also fond of *Calceolaria*, *Lavandula lanata*, *Melianthus major* and *Euryops*, especially *E. acraeus*.

Looking back, I think our main purpose has been to obtain good plants

BELOW The late Sidney Maskell with his dog Happy, enjoying a profusion of rhododendrons and azaleas. He died shortly after completing his chapter on Kilbogget.

BELOW, RIGHT Between the flagstones on the terrace are herbs and dwarf conifers. In the foreground on the left is a large *Psoralea pinnata*, covered in blue and white peaflowers, a shrub which grow outdoors in only the mildest climates.

ABOVE The view from the house across the wide, spreading lawn planted with a whitebeam and a willow-leaved pear and edged with heaths in flower.

LEFT *Tropaeolum polyphyllum* tumbling over a cushion of spruce on the stone-flagged path.

RIGHT Killiney parish church and the distant Dublin mountains from Kilbogget, with *Prunus*, *Pittosporum* and conifers in the foreground.

GLENVEAGH CASTLE
COUNTY DONEGAL

Henry P. McIlhenny

I bought Glenveagh Castle in 1937. Not only were the gardens neglected, but I found myself in a completely different horticultural world to my native Philadelphia. I had little knowledge of plants from the Himalayas, Chile and New Zealand, and had to learn how to garden with high rainfall and acid soil.

At that time the gardens consisted only of the Pleasure Ground – a large, flat area sheltered by conifers, native oak and a frightening mass of *Rhododendron ponticum*. Although neglected, it had originally been well laid out by a Kew-trained gardener. Surviving plants included an excellent specimen of *Rhododendron falconeri* and several *R. arboreum*, *Griselinia littoralis*, *Cordyline australis* and three Chusan palms. There was an overwhelming amount of bamboo, and some *Crinodendron hookerianum* to the south of the house. A *jardin potager* of vegetables and flowers for the house remained. On a higher level a path called the Belgian Walk still existed; it was built by wounded soldiers during the First World War.

These plants dated from the time the castle was built by the Adairs, in the early 1870s. Mr Adair, notorious for his evictions, died in 1885, but his widow (born Miss Wadsworth, from Geneseo, New York), continued to visit Glenveagh until just after the First World War. The next owners, from 1929–37, were Mr and Mrs A. Kingley Porter. He was a distinguished American Professor of Art at Harvard University, who disappeared mysteriously in 1933. I bought Glenveagh from his widow. It is remarkable that the house has always been owned by an American; as a result the local people have become accustomed to American habits and eccentricities!

Until 1939 my days were spent eliminating weeds, burning bamboo and cutting ivy out of the trees. During the war years I was in the Navy and the garden again became neglected; it was only after my return in 1946 that I began to be a serious gardener. My neighbours, the Earl and Countess of Leitrim, seventeen miles away at Mulroy, gave me advice, and my Harvard classmate, Lanning Roper, was a great help. In 1953 James Russell (a renowned English nurseryman) came on the scene. He had

TOP The last flight of sixty-seven stone steps up the mountainside, leading to a grass terrace with spectacular views over Lough Veagh.

apparently wild ideas which proved to be excellent, and introduced many rare and tender plants to the gardens.

Together we replanted the Pleasure Ground, the Belgian Walk, the Twelve Step Path and the View Garden. The Italian Garden, with its stone and marble sculpture from Florence, and the Swiss Walk for azaleas were created. We built a great flight of sixty-seven steps, twelve feet wide, up the mountain side to a grassy terrace overlooking the castle and the lake. We flanked the steps with profusely seeding *Rhododendron ciliatum*, and lined the top flight with lemon pots.

A wall was built round the *jardin potager* with herbaceous borders at its foot, and the paths between central beds of vegetables were edged with fruit trees (chiefly plums) and flowers for cutting. Hedging and curlicues of box were planted, giving it a Victorian atmosphere.

The old greenhouse was demolished and a neo-gothic conservatory was constructed, with an adjoining outdoor sitting room. Inside the conservatory we planted *Pelargonium*, *Mimosa*, *Datura* (angel's trumpet), *Passiflora antioquiensis* and sky-blue *Plumbago capensis*. On cold and rainy days, so frequent in Donegal, we enjoyed this warm and colourful shelter.

When Lanning Roper began working professionally, he became my advisor. His wonderful knowledge and common sense helped to bring about great improvements at Glenveagh. A flagged, walled terrace was built on the Belgian Walk, again using antique Italian sculpture and a great many terracotta pots, bought at the Impruneta pottery near Florence. One can get tired of endless naturalistic plantings, and long for formality, straight lines and hedges. The terrace was a relief to the eye because of the simplicity of its design. This, and a vista garden, just south of the castle, were my last additions. I attempted to create vistas which made architectural sense of the axial paths. I wanted to avoid having a garden beginning anywhere and ending nowhere, and preferred to plant for effect rather than to show off individual botanical specimens. Needless to say, I wanted to make more vistas and paths but Lanning Roper said, 'Don't make your garden one inch bigger; just take better care of what you've got!' – a crushing but sensible restraint.

In order to make the Pleasure Ground as exotic as possible, more palms and tree ferns and many more rhododendrons were planted. Eucalypts flourish there, as well as the large-leaved rhododendrons, which I particularly admire as they are handsome the whole year round. In other parts of the garden tender plants including *Michelia doltsopa*, *Metrosideros lucida* and fragrant *Rhododendron lindleyi* grow well.

I do not like looking at bare earth and put in a great many *Astilbe*, *Gunnera*, *Phormium* and *Rodgersia* to provide cover and contrasting foliage. Rhododendrons, succeeded by hostas, *Agapanthus* and lilies, give colour and life to the garden over a long period. Lilies were one of my specialities, and I planted an almost vulgar display of *Lilium auratum* var. *platiphyllum* to line a vista. I enjoyed the white flowers produced late in the season by large specimens of *Hoheria* and *Eucryphia*. To balance the lush green of Ireland, I like plants with white variegation in their leaves (but not the golden forms which always look unhealthy to me).

I realize that I planted too closely, and it was necessary to keep a watching eye on the more vigorous specimens to prevent them from crushing their neighbours. But in the end the density was an advantage: the congested plants were like my own nursery stock which could be transplanted to new areas.

ABOVE The *jardin potager*, transformed by Henry McIlhenny who planted the box hedges and fruit trees, and beds of vegetables and flowers for cutting.

OPPOSITE, ABOVE Antique Italian sculpture, and terracotta pots planted with Ghent azaleas and hostas, give the stone-flagged terrace on the Belgian Walk an air of timeless serenity.

OPPOSITE, BELOW The fish fountain, its urn and stone walls wreathed in *Wisteria* and *Hydrangea petiolaris*. In the distance are the crenellated towers of the castle.

LEFT A carved stone finial surmounts a wall festooned with sunlit greenery.

BELOW *Astilbe* and *Rodgersia* carpet the shady ground beneath a pink lily and the purple foliage of a Japanese maple.

The most important thing, to my mind, about the gardens of Glenveagh is that whether or not any plants are in flower there is always a spectacular view of Lough Veagh. Seen through the Scots pines, the lake surrounded by mountains looks rather like a fjord. Strong winds have always been a great menace there, and nearly every plant had to be staked. It was hard labour, but rewarding.

It was a wrench to leave Glenveagh in 1983, after so many happy years, but it is comforting to know that the gardens not only attract a large attendance but are being extremely well maintained by the State.

Henry P. McIlhenny.

KNOCK-NA-GARRY
COUNTY CORK

Mrs John Minchin

Seventeen years ago I looked gloomily at a bare half acre of stony field which faces south-south-west, with a lovely view across the river to the Royal Cork Yacht Club. Having had many years of illness, my only thought was to make that elusive creation, a trouble-free garden.

There were three whitethorns and a large privet facing the road. Otherwise we were open to all the winds, save the north and north-east; on that side we are lucky enough to have the backdrop of a wooded hill, which now belongs to the Forestry Department.

The builders laid a Liscannor stone path around two sides of the house, grudgingly leaving me a two-foot bed against the house. They also built up the hill to the south, making a flat plateau of grass. I had the idea that it would make the rather narrow end of a wedge-shaped garden look wider if one looked out over an abyss, as the field (which we don't own) slopes sharply to the river. This part of the bank has collapsed once already, but is now, I hope, held together by wild pink and white valerian.

The bungalow is below the level of the road, so the builders made retaining walls, forming two large beds bisected by a flight of steps. Walls and steps are all made of concrete bricks as unfortunately finances didn't run to anything grander, and ever since they were built I have tried to disguise them with plants hanging down to the tarmac drive, another ugly necessity. This, at last, is mellowing and also provides a home for self-sown aubrietas, *Euphorbia characias*, saxifrages, and, between cold winters, a pale pink mesembryanthemum.

A wire-netting fence used to divide us from the larger part of the field to the west, which, having supported pigs, had become a beautiful billowing hayfield. I loved to watch it while cleaning my teeth; however, there was nothing for it but to shut it away behind a substantial windbreak. Our good neighbour, from whom we bought the land, came with his tractor and moved the big privet to hide the electricity pole. He then made a trench along the fence. At that time there were only two nurseries within forty miles of Currabinny, and I bought from them any misshapen, overgrown

The view from Knock-na-Garry (which means 'the hill of the garden') looking across the Owenboy River and the sheltered harbour of Crosshaven.

and unwanted shrubs for two shillings each. I put these in the trench and the tractor shovelled back the soil. For good measure I stuck in cuttings of *Escallonia macrantha*.

Seventeen years later this mishmash has grown into a pretty, dense windbreak, but it does contain some of my more enduring mistakes, such as two Lombardy poplars. I was thrilled with them at the beginning, as they gave a little height to a flat landscape. Now they have to be topped, especially the one growing under the power lines, and their roots rush greedily all over the place. I also had a good *Viburnum × burkwoodii* which, unnoticed by me, gradually became swamped by other plants and died. To this, rightly or wrongly, I attribute an outbreak of honey fungus, which resulted in a gap in my windbreak, and I fear it is still working underground. I am fighting back with Bray's Emulsion and any shrub planted has a tablespoon of cupric carbonate (as advised by Lady Anne Palmer in *The Garden*) mixed in the soil.

The lawn was prepared and sown professionally, and from this I cut out a curved bed which is now the only trouble-free part of the garden. One curve is planted with daffodils that I brought with me when we moved from Cork City seventeen years ago, the only ones of that era to survive the depredations of the narcissus fly. On top of these I planted a collection of *Astilbe* cultivars that a friend in Connemara was throwing out. This bed gives three seasons of colour, as astilbes go a lovely honey colour in the autumn. I have only once dug up and thinned out the planting, and it is

Varieties of lily, the deep purple spikes of *Salvia* 'Superba', hostas, *Astilbe*, anemones, *Agapanthus* and hydrangeas in a rich blend of colour.

Vivid red *Callistemon* (the bottle-brush plant) and, in the foreground, *Dianthus* mixed with pale pink and purple *Veronica*.

The head of a lavender blue *Agapanthus*.

A rustic iron seat showered with the white petals of *Rubus* 'Benenden'.

only the toughest of weeds that raises its head there at any time of the year. I top-dress with bonemeal and moss peat when the leaves die down in November.

Two of my best variegated shrubs I raised as cuttings from a flower arranger's pedestal. One is the lovely *Coronilla glauca* 'Variegata', the other the golden *Griselinia littoralis* 'Bantry Bay' (my cutting was taken from the plant found by the late Murdo Mackenzie on Ilnacullin, Garinish Island. It makes a marvellous windbreak, standing four-square to protect the other part of this curved bed, which is now solid with *Artemisia arborescens*, *Hebe* 'Mrs Winder' and Knaphill azaleas. There are also gold and silver cultivars of *Euonymus fortunei* and a yellow-foliaged *Ilex crenata* to give winter colour. *Lilium pardalinum* is one of only two lilies that I am able to grow successfully: it pushes its six-foot heads through the azaleas, making a nice patch of colour against the sea when the azaleas are over. The azaleas act as useful supports for the lily stems. The bed runs along to that country necessity, the septic tank, now well shrouded in *Cotoneaster horizontalis*, *Cornus alba* 'Spaethii' and the common flowering currant, backed by one of my favourite bushes, *Amelanchier canadensis*. There is also a *Cotoneaster frigidus* which attracts the redwings in a cold winter.

In 1971 we bought the field to the west, retained a ten-yard strip, and sold the rest. The long, narrow belt that we kept was an extension of the wide end of the wedge, which was again open to the gales. I bought eight standard trees, mostly maples, from my local nurseryman, Des Nangle, who kindly came and planted them for me.

The late Hon. Mrs Bertram Bell of Fota Island in Cork Harbour had always been extremely kind and encouraging. Now that my interest was increasing she took me in hand and gave me many cuttings and seedlings, and, better still, lots of good advice. My new strip became 'The Arboretum' and has remained so in her memory. She also encouraged me to join the Royal Horticultural Society, and from its monthly magazines I have acquired a little more knowledge.

Never having lived in any one place for a long period, I had never been a collector, but suddenly I found myself coveting plants in other people's gardens. This trait has got worse over the years, and it is becoming increasingly difficult to find a home for new treasures. Gardeners are a kind and generous race, and I have been given good plants by many people, but when I look around here I realize that the large majority came from Mrs Betty Farquhar of Ardsallagh, County Tipperary, who has made one of the greatest gardens since the war. From her I have learnt much and am still learning, and I still covet many of her treasures!

I had long wanted a pool so that I could grow water lilies. I think my love of them dates back nearly sixty years, when I won a prize for a never-to-be-forgotten flower arrangement of white water lilies in a black bowl. Eventually, two years ago, a pool was built. It gives us a lot of pleasure, but it is hard to preserve the goldfish as we are in the flight path of large numbers of herons, who fish the slobland below. The pool has opened up an area where I can grow herbaceous perennials and small rockery plants which hitherto got lost. There is a nice damp corner for small ferns and, of course, lots more work.

Now that I have reasonable shelter on three sides, it is possible to grow many tender plants, and I suspect some, such as the cultivars of *Correa*, are hardier than their reputation suggests. *Brachyglottis repanda* 'Purpurea' took a beating this last winter, but is sprouting again; I would hate to lose its exceptionally handsome foliage. *Dodonaea viscosa* 'Purpurea' was also battered but is now reviving. *Restio subverticillatus* was quite untouched, even a small piece that I had moved into a more open area. A young tree fern from Rossdohan, County Kerry, is looking well, and nearby, after trying it all round the garden, the handsome Chatham Island forget-me-not (*Myosotidium hortensia*) seems happy.

Fremontodendron mexicanum grows on the south wall of the house, but cannot cope with the wind. The leaves look maggoty all the year round, except where a branch has grown into the shelter of a bedroom window recess. *Jacobinia pauciflora* is not often seen, but it does well here, even after cold winters. Quite by chance I acquired *Bowkeria gerardiana*. One has to make an expedition down the garden to study its curious, waxy orchid-like flowers; it was planted in the wrong place, but has survived the winter and maybe next autumn I shall risk moving it nearer a path.

I spend a fortune on clematis, trying to get them to grow through shrubs and trees, as I now have so little space in the flowerbeds. A lot die through my bad planting and subsequent neglect, but many are making their way, much to my delight.

Until I got the pool the only places I had in which to grow small treasures were three very old stone troughs, their sides worn where axes were sharpened years ago. *Ramonda myconi* and *R. nathaliae* look well with self-seeding *Erinus alpinus*. I have several *Sempervivum* cultivars and a number of self-sown seedlings of a good *Euryops acraeus* which died last year.

I am often asked which is my favourite flower. Not being a specialist in anything, and still very unsure of my botanical facts, I simply don't have one. I love each one as its season comes round, and am eternally grateful that I have stumbled into such an absorbing and happy hobby.

Nancy Lauder

KILMOKEA
COUNTY WEXFORD

David Price

If you were brought up to enjoy a delightful house surrounded by a garden that complements it, you will perhaps wonder why we bought a dilapidated old rectory without water and electricity, and with a garden containing only a dozen apple trees and a quarter of an acre of potatoes. However, the house, built in 1794, had lovely rooms, and a neighbourly dowser was able to assure us that there was an inexhaustible supply of water within three yards of the back door. So my wife and I considered that it would be a good investment.

As for the garden, we could create a new one with our own selection of plants. Since my father's gardening days, before the First World War, many exciting trees and shrubs had been discovered in faraway places, including Chile, China and the Himalayas. We quickly learnt that the old rectory garden was a mild one, kept frost free by the warm waters of the Barrow estuary that surround it on three sides.

I believe in formality round a house, and also that the bare bones of the garden – walls, paths and hedges – should give twelve months of pleasure. If you depend solely on trees and shrubs for colour and interest, you will find there are periods in the year when the garden offers little excitement. Here we have delightful local stone for walls, old paving stones from the streets of New Ross for paths, and an endless variety of hedges.

There are hedges of yew, which many people think is slow growing, but it does well if started with rich manure. Years ago I went to a nursery where a line of large *Prunus cerasifera* 'Nigra' had been cut down to three feet six inches, and immediately I realized this plant's value as a hedge; it has pink buds in March followed by delightful red foliage. There is also a splendid windbreak of *Crinodendron*, now twelve feet high. We use shrub roses, for example *Rosa rugosa* 'Blanc Double de Coubert', as a floriferous hedge, and we have a good hedge of *Luma apiculata* crowned with the red flowers of *Tropaeolum speciosum*. I am fond of the mixtures you can make with yew, golden yew and beech. All these different hedges give shape and form to the garden.

Water is life in a garden: its sound, its beauty and its usefulness make it an essential element. The most important feature at Kilmokea is the natural spring, which flows under the road to the lower garden, into a large mill pool much enjoyed by ducks, and on through the main garden, giving us enormous pleasure.

The front door of the house looks out on to a square area of beds, grass and paths surrounded by a holly hedge. Through the wall to the left, past the dovecote, is a small plantation of camellias and a rock garden, in whose foundations we found many oyster shells; the former inhabitants of the old rectory must have lived well. When we first came here in 1946 the river was rich in salmon and trout, and there were plenty of partridges and pheasants, as well as a goose slob below the house. Alas, owing to pollution, all this has now gone.

Through the yew hedge is the Italian garden, with its loggia and pool, at the end of which stands the small bronze figure of a man, pouring what should be wine from the pigskin under his arm. All these ideas were introduced by Harold Peto, a relative, who designed glorious gardens, including Ilnacullin (Garinish Island) in Bantry Bay and many in northern Italy.

Beside the loggia are large specimens of *Magnolia* × *soulangiana*, overlooked by the beautiful *M. campbellii* var. *mollicomata*; there are sixteen different species and cultivars of *Magnolia* in the garden. We have now

PREVIOUS PAGE The Italianate loggia, surrounded by large specimens of *Magnolia*, provides a focus to the pool garden which is planted with roses and *Verbascum*.

OPPOSITE, ABOVE A peacock on a yew hedge in the topiary garden behind the house, and beyond it the beautiful old stone dovecote.

OPPOSITE, BELOW David Price at work, mixing compost.

reached the back of the house and can saunter past my wife's herbaceous border. This is out of bounds to me, and I am delighted to leave it in her hands. Between the herbaceous garden and the lupin border which faces it is one of the rose beds and a group of tree peonies.

At the back of the house there are numerous examples of topiary. I know of few topiary gardens in Ireland, which is sad: it is an interesting art and helps to provide form and structure in a garden, and it is not a great labour; the young yew tree itself helps to suggest how it should be clipped, and what form it should take.

At the bottom of the main garden is a fine specimen of *Magnolia × soulangiana* 'Lennei', overlooked by a large Chilean fire bush (*Embothrium coccineum*), which can be seen from the house. A right turn takes you over the quiet road to the lower garden which I started eighteen years ago, planting saplings of spruce, Japanese larch, hemlock and Douglas fir seven feet apart. They have helped to dry out what was fundamentally a bog, and their drainage work has been aided by trenches cut to carry water into the central stream.

A mass of white flowers on a *Clematis montana* makes a bower for a classical stone head.

ABOVE A traditional herbaceous border, which runs along the wall of an ancient graveyard. It has been cleverly planned so that no plant obscures another and colours blend harmoniously.

Pink Candelabra primulas provide a vivid display in the woodland garden, where they flourish in the damp conditions.

A path to the left leads past mounds of blue hydrangeas, many of them 'Blue Wave'. On the opposite side of a nearby pool are different cultivars of *Cotoneaster*, which provide colour from October to the beginning of January. There are also many willows, the perfect complement to water.

Below the dam that contains the pool is a group of *Eucryphia*, which give us much pleasure in August. We are fortunate in being able to grow most of the different cultivars: we have a small plant of *Eucryphia moorei* that seems to be a rare species in cultivation; the only other plant I know – a fine specimen protected by two walls – is at Rowallane, County Down. I am fond of the myrtle family, but the bad winter of 1978 rather reduced them. In spring there are numerous lovely rhododendrons, and nearly fifty different camellias that are a joy to cut for the house. All through this damp and fertile garden grow candelabra primulas, shown off by the blue of *Omphalodes cappadocica*.

Kilmokea now extends to eight acres. I don't think our enthusiasm can take us any further, but each year we add to our collection of maples, and these, in time, will contribute greatly to the beauty of the garden.

Dairis E. C. Price.

8, CLUNE ROAD, FINGLAS
COUNTY DUBLIN

Mrs Kitty Reardon

My small garden was originally part of rich pastureland. A dairy firm, which produced milk and butter for its city customers, grazed herds on this land for almost seventy years, before selling it for development.

I remember the day when I came with my husband, Liam, to see the house we were about to buy. It was the lovely plot of garden attached to it that really took my fancy: all the wonderful things that could be grown

LEFT Columbines, lilies and pinks abound in this summer border. In the foreground, *Campanula* blend beautifully with *Tradescantia*.

OPPOSITE A Spanish broom overhangs a border in which lilies take pride of place; around them are tobacco plants (*Nicotiana*), *Dicentra spectabilis*, *Fuchsia* and *Calceolaria*.

there kept appearing in my imagination, and I could hardly wait to get a spade into the earth.

As the soil was alkaline, I knew that rhododendrons would never be happy. Instead *Mahonia*, *Spiraea* and some early-flowering *Berberis* were planted. Shrubs with colourful foliage, such as variegated hollies, *Elaeagnus*, *Corokia*, and a golden-leaved *Berberis* soon found a place in the garden.

Those early plantings are all thriving today, thanks to the thorough job done by Liam when preparing the site for them. He was a firm believer in giving them a 'good start', which meant a generous ration of manure for each plant. We put in ten apple trees, two Victoria plum trees, and currant and gooseberry bushes, never giving a thought to the day when they would grow up and overcrowd each other.

A fine selection of vegetables was produced, and we proudly shared the surplus with our friends. Potatoes, peas and giant cauliflowers took up much of the space, and their leaves and stalks made good cover for the boys who got in to steal the apples.

I joined the local horticultural society, and exhibited some of the vegetables at its annual show. Winning a first prize in a class for five onions started me on my career as an exhibitor. I wanted to grow and exhibit dahlias as well as vegetables, but lack of shelter limited me to the small-flowered cultivars. Roses did well, even in this rather windswept situation, and we planted about a hundred bushes to provide colour as well as nice blooms for exhibition.

The glasshouse erected on one side of the garden path provides shelter from westerly winds for a border about forty feet long, in which are planted all the old cottage garden favourites. Delphiniums look down on foxgloves, columbines, peonies, carnations, pinks and stocks, making a colourful and fragrant border in early summer. On the side opposite the glasshouse, a hedge of golden privet provides a background for phlox, golden rod, Solomon's seal, *Thalictrum*, *Lobelia cardinalis* and the chimney bell-flower, *Campanula pyramidalis*. Shrubs with variegated foliage, such as *Hoheria*, *Teucrium*, *Pittosporum*, myrtle and *Hebe* cultivars also flourish in this sheltered border.

Nearer the house is a small raised bed about fifteen inches high containing plants that could be classified as unusual, contrary and just ordinary. Precious little plants given to me by gardening friends find a home here, contrary ones have the benefit of attention, and the little ordinary ones – crocuses, pansies and pinks – provide bright splashes of colour.

Before the next border could be laid out two of the apple trees had to be felled. We hoped to plant this area so that it would provide colour from early spring to late autumn. Daffodil and tulip bulbs, about a dozen at a time, were planted along it in groups. Bold clumps of hostas went in beside them, along with *Agapanthus* and Guernsey lilies.

Lilies take pride of place in this border, producing colour and perfume throughout the summer months. The first lily to bloom is 'Red Bird', followed by 'Pink Corsage', *Lilium regale*, 'Citronella' and 'Golden Splendor', and then, in late summer, *L. speciosum* var. *rubrum*. When the tulip and daffodil foliage dies down I put pots and urns filled with fuchsias or pelargoniums in the empty spaces. It is easy to conceal the pots among the clumps of hostas – small standard fuchsias look good with an apron of striped hosta foliage – and the pots help to keep the nasty little narcissus fly from damaging the bulbs during the summer.

Kitty Reardon working in her glasshouse, which overflows with fuchsias, *Hippeastrum* and a host of colourful pelargoniums.

BELOW Sunlit cottage garden flowers – daisies, campanulas, fuchsias, lupins and lilies – spill over a narrow path between packed shrubs in this small city garden.

The time came when the apple trees finally lost the battle against the shrubs and flowers. Four more trees were removed, which seemed a shame as they were cropping well. The gooseberry bushes had to go too, because for two years in succession they were attacked by dreadful caterpillars togged out in black and amber – like our local football team. The speed with which they devour foliage is really amazing.

When flower arranging became one of my hobbies, it did much to make the garden look more interesting. Shape and colour of foliage became important in choosing what to plant. Shrubs such as *Stephanandra tanakae*, *Itea ilicifolia*, *Rosa glauca*, *Choisya ternata* and *Cotinus coggyria* are now living happily in the former gooseberry patch. Some ferns and small evergreens find room there too. Both the purple-leaved and variegated cultivars of New Zealand flax were planted in sheltered positions and are doing well. The brightly coloured ivy 'Goldheart' has covered a lot of the fence between my garden and that of my neighbour. It has now climbed about thirty feet up my neighbour's holly tree, closely followed by her climbing rose 'Joseph's Coat'. My *Clematis* 'Nelly Moser' makes a beautiful display on the fence during early summer; I must treat myself to another plant of this old favourite before the year is out.

The greenhouse gives protection to a wide range of potted plants. *Pelargonium* and *Fuchsia* fill much of the staging as I like to exhibit them at the local shows during the summer. They are also useful for filling colourless gaps in the outside borders. 'Happy Thought' is an excellent pelargonium for this purpose, with colourful foliage and single flowers that are not damaged by bad weather.

Through the years I have acquired a good collection of *Fuchsia*. If a thorough search was made, it might be possible to locate about sixty cultivars here. Some are planted in the garden and are cut back annually by frosts, but they always appear again and flower well in late July and August. The potted ones spend late summer and autumn outside as well, where they do best in positions shaded from strong sunlight. They enjoy wet summers, when the flowers are much larger than usual.

Sharing and exchanging plants is one of the real pleasures of gardening, and I would like to think that we gardeners would always be ready to share our knowledge and plants with beginners.

During the summer I looked round the garden and decided that there was no more space available for planting, not even for the most tempting shrub. As Liam is no longer with me to help with the various jobs, I find that keeping the garden in order takes up a great amount of time. This promise to myself is a difficult one to keep. In early August I ordered a hundred bulbs of daffodils and tulips. They are to arrive on the first of September.

Kitty Reardon

CASTLEMARTIN
COUNTY KILDARE
Mrs Tony O'Reilly

We bought Castlemartin in 1972. Although the present house, built in 1720 on the site of a medieval castle, was in need of restoration, we fell in love with it, and with the surrounding park and the River Liffey meandering through the valley below.

As there was no garden, we asked the great landscape architect Lanning Roper to design one for us. We told him that we wanted a scented garden, and one that was interesting most of the year. He came here in 1973, and not only landscaped the park but also planted many of the trees and shrubs himself. James Kelly, our farm manager since 1968, worked with Lanning as planting was carried out. He knows every tree and shrub here, and keeps a fatherly eye on them. He said that Lanning was a joy to work with, and had a great appreciation of nature, the soil, and everything that grew.

The main entrance gates, archway and railings of the estate, handmade in an ornate leaf design, are reputed to be among the finest examples of wrought-iron work in Ireland. Throughout the parkland and on each side of the drive are informal groups of maples, mountain ash and bird cherry, and fine specimen trees including cut-leaved beech and blue cedar. An avenue of lime trees sweeps up to the side of the house. Lanning planted a formal beech hedge on either side of the forecourt, with an open vista to the lime tree walk, which is carpeted with sheets of snowdrops in early spring. This avenue of limes has been here for 150 years; at one end it is flanked by a pair of standard golden ash trees (*Fraxinus excelsior* 'Jaspidea').

On the north lawn is a fountain, and my husband Tony likes to listen to the sound of its running water as he works near the library window. Quite close to the fountain we planted silver birch trees, the autumn-flowering cherry, and the yellow-berried rowan 'Joseph Rock' which has wonderful red leaves in the autumn. My own private place is a small walled garden nearby. Lanning knew that I had been brought up in Australia, sometimes living in outback towns where there was always a lovely garden. I grew up among roses, figs, almonds and citrus orchards. I wanted a similar garden, and flowers to cut for the house. But it is too cold at Castlemartin for most of

ABOVE Castlemartin, seen from the lupin border in the cutting garden.

ABOVE RIGHT Old-fashioned roses clothe the wall of a flight of granite steps up to the house.

LEFT Susan O'Reilly at Castlemartin, arranging lilies, rhododendron leaves and *Gypsophila* cut from the garden.

the plants we grew in Australia, so my garden is planted with roses – 'Peace', 'Grandpa Dickson', 'Pink Favourite', 'Ena Harkness' and 'Pascali'. We put in a long row of sweet peas, lupins in many colours, peonies, *Gypsophila*, *Sidalcea* 'Loveliness', and some of my favourite lilies – *Lilium regale*, *L. longiflorum* 'White Queen' and 'Mount Everest'. There is also a large selection of herbs and vegetables for the kitchen. I love to get up early and pick the flowers with the dew still on them.

On the north side of the house is the pool courtyard, an important part of the garden where Tony and I can sit and relax. The pool was created in the old stable yard. A converted cottage used as a guesthouse, smothered in silver-pink flowers of the rose 'New Dawn', looks on to the pool and the river beyond. Flowerbeds at the foot of the surrounding walls contain a luxuriant planting in soft colours of the pineapple-scented Moroccan broom, *Pittosporum tenuifolium* 'James Stirling', Mexican orange blossom and the blue-green leaves of *Rosa glauca* (once called *Rosa rubrifolia*), enhanced by *Berberis thunbergii* 'Atropurpurea Nana' and *Senecio* 'Sunshine', underplanted with blue *Agapanthus*, English *Iris* and cranesbills. White jasmine, ivies and *Clematis montana* 'Rubens' scramble over the walls.

The banks of the lawn have been lowered considerably, revealing a beautiful view of the river from the house. Honeysuckles and *Cotoneaster* screen the wire fence of the nearby tennis court, and the surrounding area is planted with *Euonymus fortunei* 'Silver Queen', *Syringa* 'Madame Lemoine' and 'Charles Joly', *Hydrangea paniculata* 'Grandiflora', *Philadelphus* 'Virginal', and more roses – 'Fru Dagmar Hastrup' and 'Frühlingsgold'. A pair of 'Grey Owl' junipers flank the granite steps from the tennis court.

Lanning liked scented flowers. Throughout the herbaceous border beneath the breakfast room window he mixed night-scented stock, white-flowered tobacco, lavender, rosemary and thyme. Other favourite herbaceous plants in this bed include *Alchemilla mollis*, *Sedum spectabile*, *Stachys olympica* 'Silver Carpet', hostas, and roses 'Peace' and 'Queen Elizabeth'.

LEFT Complementing the grey stone of the clock tower in the stable yard are the pale apricot flowers of the rose 'Buff Beauty' and the cream plumes of *Rodgersia aesculifolia*.

The guest house, its walls almost entirely covered by the delicate rose 'New Dawn'. In the foreground is the fragrant 'Blanc Double de Coubert'.

An elegant iron gate swathed in clematis, red honeysuckle and roses leads to an open lawn which runs down to the River Liffey.

In the spring we look on to thousands of daffodils, and beyond them the river, curving its way towards Dublin and the Irish Sea. All the trees and plants have brought back the birds and butterflies. The garden is heavenly, and it is a tribute to Lanning.

Castlemartin is steeped in history. With the help of Percy Le Clerq we have faithfully restored the fifteenth-century church dedicated to St Mary that stands within the demesne. For five centuries and more it has been a tree-planted haven.

It is remarkable to realize that Robert Brown, the greatest botanist of the nineteenth century, walked here in the autumn of 1800, collecting grasses by the Liffey's banks, and lichens and mosses from the trees. And it was at Castlemartin, on the morning of 17 December 1800, that this young Scotsman, an army surgeon, received a summons from Sir Joseph Banks to join HMS *Investigator* on her great voyage. One year later Robert Brown stepped on to Australia's parched earth, and today he is widely considered the 'Father of Australian Botany'. He left his footprints in my native land – and here too, in my Irish garden.

Susan O'Reilly

BUTTERSTREAM
COUNTY MEATH
Jim Reynolds

I knew little of gardening, but was beginning to develop an interest, when I was offered a temporary position that involved visits to National Trust properties in Scotland and England. I was then a precocious under-graduate and my first call in the south of England was to Sissinghurst. I viewed the garden and climbed the tower in less than half an hour, and presented myself to my host, Nigel Nicolson. He seemed rather taken aback that I had seen everything. A later perusal of a guide-book, and a more leisurely walk, showed that there was a little more to the place than my first impressions had conveyed. However I was not intimidated and felt, optimistically, that I too could have a garden like that – though not perhaps on the same scale: if Vita Sackville-West and her husband Harold Nicolson could make something magical out of a wilderness, so could I.

Back home in Ireland I visited as many gardens as possible in search of further inspiration: Birr Castle, County Offaly, and Mount Stewart, County Down, were early favourites. 'Think big' was my motto. I read what came my way – Lanning Roper, Vita Sackville-West and Graham Stuart Thomas – and, I regret to say, learned very little; most of my knowledge has come expensively, through experience.

The site of the garden had been part of an old flood plain, and is relatively low-lying. The stream which traversed this plain, en route to the nearby River Boyne, had been confined to a narrow channel in the seventeenth century, but not before it had reduced the depth of boulder clay by several feet. The area is fortunately bordered by a few mature trees – beech, ash and sycamore, the common hedgerow trees of County Meath. In between were some old farm buildings, open drains, and old field banks supporting fine hedges of elder and brambles. I set to work. Drains had to be laid, filled in or diverted, scrubby hedges dug out, banks levelled, and two small farm buildings had to be removed. Being penniless, I could employ neither man nor machine, so embarked on this mammoth task alone, armed with spade and shovel, saw and sledgehammer. During

weekends and evenings I pushed onwards, encouraged by my mother, herself a keen gardener, who sadly did not live to see the results.

First I made three compartments divided by beech hedges. The central area was to be a rose garden: old fashioned roses, of course – Alba, Bourbon, Damask, Gallica and moss roses in subtle shades of pink, mauve, red and white. No virulent scarlet hybrid teas and floribunda roses for me. Several plants, including 'Souvenir de la Princesse de Lamballe', 'Rosa mundi' and the Jacobite rose, 'Alba Maxima', were rescued from old gardens. Gradually the collection increased as I tracked down more and more plants in English nurseries, or even by the side of the road, until it flowed into other parts of the garden.

The roses were planted in formal beds, divided by paths of limestone pebbles and bordered by boxwood hedges. The first box plants, ordered in 1970 from a once famous northern nursery, arrived looking moth-eaten to say the least. They were remnants of an ancient box hedge which had been dug up, chopped into pieces and dumped on me. I washed the roots, attempting to remove all the suspicious-looking white stringy pieces with which they were covered and, ever an optimist, I planted it. Results came quickly, and by early summer I had a glorious hedge of scutch grass. I was now learning fast, and remembered the advice of Vita Sackville-West to be utterly ruthless (if only I could apply this in other fields, life would be quite different), so I dug it out and burned it. Fortunately I soon found an excellent source of box in a nearby nursery at Summerhill. The strong young plants soon settled down and grew well, in spite of the constant attention of four dogs.

Beneath the roses I planted crown imperials, peonies, lilies, *Crinum* and *Nerine* to extend the rather short season of the rose garden. Of the other two compartments, one has been planted as a white garden, its boxwood hedges and formal paths centred on an eighteenth-century sundial and a Victorian gothic seat; the other has mainly herbaceous plants in hot colours, which flower after rose time. Luckily, this planting scheme worked fairly well, and gave me much-needed encouragement to push on.

Outside the outer beech hedges I planted *Camellia*, *Rhododendron*, *Embothrium*, *Callistemon*, *Drimys*, *Hoheria* and *Eucryphia*. After all, these are the plants which thrive in the mild climate of Ireland, or so the garden books would have the innocent believe. Then, as now, most books aimed at the British or American public have the frequent aside, 'This will thrive in mild coastal areas such as Ireland'. Even though the soil here is limestone based, I assured myself that these plants would grow, given liberal additions of peat and occasional applications of sequestrene. However, I was soon faced with grim reality. While I might not have felt the cold, the plants certainly did. The garden is a frost pocket in the coldest part of Ireland. The soil, a heavy clay, is frequently waterlogged and there is constant wind from the west and south-west. Such perversities only added to the challenge, as did the occasional invasion of marauding cattle. These, I told myself, were minor difficulties to be overcome – all part of the rich tapestry of life.

Gradually the boundaries were pushed back until over two acres of farm land had been included in the garden. I was obliged to move slowly; there was, and still is, no help. I am a five to nine gardener, and rather regret that eight hours of the day are spent elsewhere in pursuit of a meagre crust. Shortage of money I discovered to be a distinct advantage: like many before me, I could make the most appalling mistakes if cash flowed too

TOP The tall spires of apricot and cream *Eremurus* are a spectacular sight in early summer.

PREVIOUS PAGE An axial path and the formal planting of boxwood in the white garden lead the eye from the eighteenth-century sundial to a Victorian gothic seat.

TOP Lavender and *Alchemilla mollis* carpet the ground in this informal corner of the garden.

ABOVE Clipped box hedges and a collection of old-fashioned roses, reminiscent of the great garden at Sissinghurst which first inspired Jim Reynolds.

freely. Far better to plan carefully, thinking each new venture out slowly. Then I can decide just what is essential and what can be dispensed with. Being something of a Luddite I use the minimal amount of machinery, a lawn mower and an occasional hedge trimmer being my only mechanical aids. The latter I regard with deep suspicion, fine for cutting thorn hedges but much too insensitive for beech or box.

Because of its irregular shape, the garden falls naturally into a series of distinct areas. These divisions have been accentuated by planting to create particular themes and moods. One informally planted enclosure is filled with shrubs, various rose species and small trees. The larger trees play host to climbing roses such as 'Bobbie James', 'Paul's Himalayan Musk Rambler', 'Sanders' White Rambler' and *Rosa filipes*. Underplanting here includes primulas, blue poppies, ferns, astilbes and hostas. I confess I was an early victim of 'hosta-fever' – even prepared to cross the Atlantic for new varieties. Fortunately I am recovering: the great avalanche of new cultivars, many over-priced, of little merit and scarcely different from older forms, has helped to cure me.

An area of grass paths beyond the white garden is bordered by herbaceous planting, foxtail lilies (*Eremurus*) being one of the main early summer features. *Monarda*, *Phlox*, *Campanula* and *Crocosmia* also grow particularly well in the heavy clay. The ground here, as in all parts of this labour-intensive garden, must be weeded by hand, a most satisfying business. How I hate the visits of pseudo-gardeners who moan, 'But you have no time to enjoy the garden'. Why should one not enjoy the physical work involved?

Beyond the herbaceous borders an open area of grass provides a welcome contrast to the confined spaces, tall hedges, overhanging trees and narrow paths which characterize the rest of the garden. Hidden to one side of this lawn was a 'Cinderella' corner, a resting place for an assemblage of plants that seemed to be permanently homeless. These stateless beings have now been ruthlessly dispersed, and a Roman garden is taking shape. A formal pool has been set in a wide pavement, flanked by pots of clipped bay and box and enclosed by box hedges, with a Tuscan temple at the end. Already there are problems: the vulgar orange carp clash horribly with the deep pink flowers of the water lily 'Escarboucle', which was acquired at considerable cost. One or other must go. How much better would be some of those sophisticated blue-black fish that inhabit the pond at Beech Park!

The temple had a previous existence as the portico of a Georgian lodge. After eighteen months of haggling, the owner relented and sold the ruin. With the aid of my sister and brothers, I dismantled it in a weekend and carried it to its new position, where it was re-erected with much pushing, heaving and praying. Surrounded on all sides by the ruins of Georgian Ireland, one might think that architectural features and fragments could be easily obtained. Far from it; when the owner of a crumbling ruin is approached, his previously worthless stones immediately appreciate in value. The would-be purchaser is assured that the broken columns and stones are worth thousands of pounds, and that he has already refused outrageous offers from a dozen clients. However, I should not complain. Vigilance and perseverance, some would say stubborness, have paid off, and I have been able to rescue numerous *objets trouvés* to adorn the place in new guises.

There is, of course, much more to be done. The garden is never static, not just growing and changing with the seasons, but changing in form and

Foxgloves in shades of pink, mauve and cream arch upwards under sycamore trees in one of the long borders.

An old water pump and an oval stone trough, over which ferns spray graceful pale green fronds.

The red and yellow garden, seen through an arch of beech, with orange lilies, lemon day lilies and the tall red Jerusalem Cross *(Lychnis chalcedonica)*.

content: old plants and sometimes trees are discarded for something different; new areas and vistas are opened up, a building or a gate revealed, or a new border made. This is the part I really enjoy. Fortunately passing years do not make me wiser – only more reckless and impractical.

Jim Reynolds

CHARLEVILLE
COUNTY WICKLOW

Mrs Kenneth Rohan

Years ago I went to a party at Charleville; I remember I was stunned by the beauty of the place. I was terribly excited therefore when in 1982, while my husband Ken and I were searching for a house, we were informed that Charleville might be for sale. We went to look at it. After driving up a long avenue of lime and beech trees we rounded a bend, glimpsed the house and fell in love with it. When we saw a little of the garden and walked down the front field, with its lovely view of the valley beyond the trees, and Powerscourt House in the distance with the fountain playing, it all seemed so beautiful that we decided to buy it then and there.

Charleville had belonged to the Monck family since 1705. The original house was destroyed by fire in 1792 and Charles Stanley, Viscount Monck, built the New House as it was called. It was completed by 1799 and has been described as 'a handsome mansion of granite, the front of which is in Palladian style'. The rooms have beautiful ceilings and cornices and their original solid mahogany doors.

A large walled garden, curved on the west side, lies behind the house. It is divided in half by a long stone wall and there is a conservatory in the middle. Michael Meaney, who knew the garden before 1927, when Lord Monck was alive, remembered that there had been two long vineries on either side of this conservatory, but by the time we came here the vineries had gone and the building was a ruin.

Outside the walled garden are the pleasure grounds, with some large old trees and an orchard full of ancient apple trees. According to the great horticulturist Graham Stuart Thomas, who visited Charleville recently, the straight *allées* in the garden denote seventeenth-century design.

The garden is magical, and is lovingly cared for by Anthony Doyle, the head steward, who has worked here full time since 1941, and John Stevens, who has been here for twenty years. We asked Helen Dillon for advice on the garden, and she introduced us to the plantsman Arthur Shackleton, who is overseeing the restoration with Ken. Ken wanted to do something new as well as to preserve the old, and Arthur comes regularly and gives

ABOVE Virgin snow covers the ground in this view of the avenue of Irish yews. The conservatory has now been restored to its original elegance and filled with sweet-scented climbing plants.

Verbascum soar over the wispy spikes of giant oats (*Stipa gigantea*) in the summer border which is overlooked by a Regency trellis-work pavilion.

An orchard of ancient apple trees in the pleasure grounds that surround the walled garden.

invaluable advice.

A formal avenue of mature Irish yews, planted in pairs, leads down to the focal point of the garden, the early nineteenth-century conservatory. This has been restored recently, using much of the original glass. It is planted with many scented flowers – I particularly wanted to be able to walk inside and smell the sweet scent of jasmine – and Arthur produced a list of many fragrant climbers as well as plants grown for colour: *Jasminum polyanthum*, *Datura* (angel's trumpet), which is superbly scented, *Buddleja madagascariensis*, with yellow flowers in winter, *Acacia pravissima* (mimosa), *Erythrina crista-galli*, with scarlet pea-shaped flowers, and blue *Plumbago capensis*. There are other shrubs and climbers including pelargoniums, fuchsias and ferns, and a large group of *Heliotropium peruvianum* (cherry pie). It was interesting to hear from Michael Meaney about the planting in the conservatory in former years. He told us there had been a large white *Datura* in the central bed, surrounded by jasmine, and a wisteria had also been planted there because it was considered too tender to be grown outside. Rose 'Gloire de Dijon' and cherry pie grew near the doorway.

The rose garden has beech hedges on two sides, one forming a beech tunnel, and on the east side a high yew hedge. There used to be a series of small beds but these were impossible to keep tidy, so now we have only four large ones with a mixture of roses. In the middle is a small pavilion linked to two pergolas.

Autumn sees the leaves of a tulip tree (*Liriodendron tulipifera*) turn golden and fall.

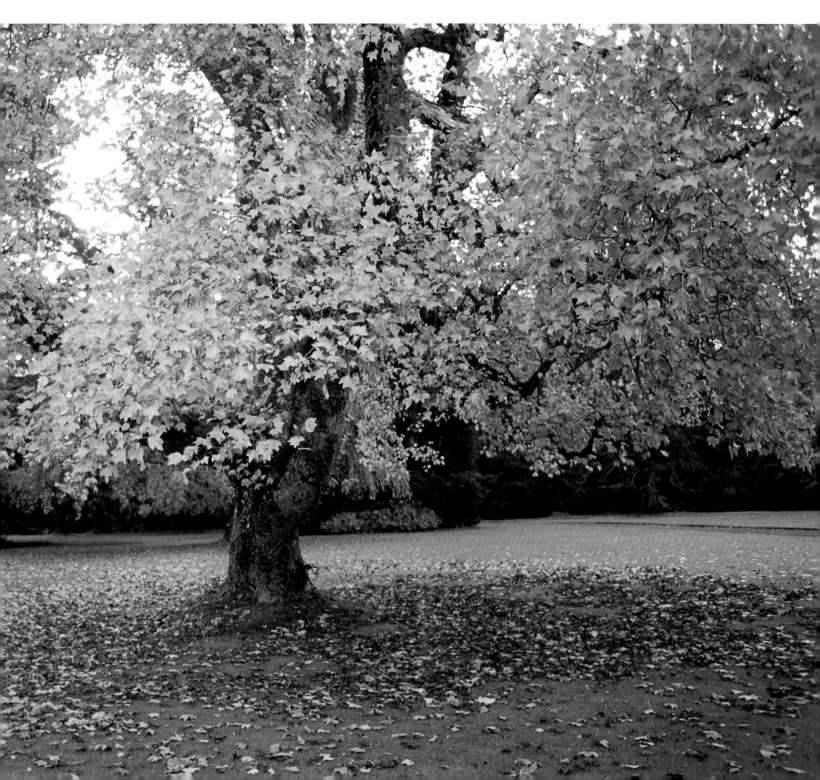

The beech tunnel is about two hundred years old. It is lovely in spring, when the new growth is fresh green and wild garlic is in bloom underneath. In winter the old, gnarled branches are equally beautiful. The tunnel leads to a door in the wall of the kitchen garden. Elizabeth Batt (daughter of Charles Monck) told me the origins of two myrtle trees planted on either side of this door. One was grown from a sprig taken from the wedding bouquet of Lady Elizabeth Scott, who married Henry, fifth Viscount Monck, on 23 July 1874. The other is a myrtle raised from a sprig in the bouquet of Mary Portal, who married Captain the Hon. Charles Monck on 15 February 1904. Sadly, he never inherited Charleville as he was killed in the First World War.

At the other end, the beech tunnel joins up with the yew hedge, which will have to be pruned aggressively this autumn, following the advice of Graham Stuart Thomas.

On the north side of the garden we have built a tennis court, overlooked by a small pavilion and terrace. Beyond is the old herbaceous border which has been replanted with astilbes, delphiniums, cranesbills, lupins, sedum and many other good perennial plants, including grasses: the large clumps of *Stipa gigantea* are particularly fine, with beautiful heads of brown oats. On either side of the conservatory are beds of azaleas and shrubs. We have planted a lime walk here, which will be pleached, and there are flowering cherries, clematis, *Vitis vinifera* 'Brant' (a vine with good autumn colouring) and *Actinidia kolomikta*, a climber with variegated leaves of pink, white and green.

Behind the dividing wall is the old circular vegetable garden, with two huge fig trees. We are planning to make a water garden here as the large quantity of vegetables that used to be grown long ago is unnecessary. The apple trees, draped with huge bunches of mistletoe, will remain but most of the new planting will be of shrubs. We hope this garden will develop slowly over the years.

In the pleasure grounds we have kept most of the original planting, but the rotten trees and smothering brambles have gone. The stumps were ground down, the weeds cleared, and we planted *Davidia involucrata* (the handkerchief or dove tree), the cut-leaved beech and *Quercus coccinea* 'Splendens' (the scarlet oak).

The magnificent broad walk, running through the pleasure grounds, was made in 1851 to commemorate the Great Exhibition in London. It is lovely to walk between the fine deodars, redwoods and cedars of Lebanon, or along the paths that wind through the shrubbery. Nearby are the site of the first house and a dogs' graveyard under a weeping ash. A sense of history is completed by a story told by Michael Meaney about the pine tree facing the drawing-room window. It was planted by Gladstone in 1877 – a fact that was once recorded on a commemorative plaque which, it is said, Henry, Lord Monck, who hated Gladstone, threw into the middle of the Irish Sea!

Brendan Rohan

The twisting branches of two-hundred-year-old beech trees.

ISHLAN
COUNTY ANTRIM
Mrs Noel Sanderson

It all started with the pond. We had moved into a house with a one-acre garden and were concerned that the view from the drawing-room window was unsatisfying, formless. 'What we need', said my husband Noel, 'is a focal point.' I was greatly impressed by this observation. 'What about a pond?' he continued.

So a pond ten feet by twenty feet with a surrounding terrace, was constructed. We built retaining walls, granite dry-stone walls, broad steps going down to the pond and further steps and paths leading away, all in shades of grey. Now the focal point aroused pangs of dismay: I knew I had to discover how to soften and break up this monotony. I asked my next door neighbour, who had a good garden, what to do. His advice was to subscribe to a weekly gardening magazine, join a local garden society, talk to local gardeners, visit all gardens open to the public and ask questions. He also introduced me to the Royal Horticultural Society.

It was not long before I discovered the destructive force of wind, and that nearly everything needed staking. When I saw that there was an Alpine Garden Society mentioned in the *Journal of the Royal Horticultural Society*, I decided that this was the very thing for me: no need to stake rock plants. My first meeting, in Belfast, was addressed by Will Ingwersen. Could anyone have been luckier? But there was a whole new language to assimilate – *Androsace*, moraine, cliff dweller, *Gentiana*, scree and tufa. I still had no intention of dropping my golf or tennis, but the garden was winning. I found at this meeting that I was among an enthusiastic and dedicated community of plantsmen, whose interest and knowledge ranged from high alpines to forest trees; I could feel myself being caught up.

The soil in the garden was stiff, sticky clay, neutral to slightly alkaline. The land sloped away from the house to the south and the west. The southern slope, terraced by the previous owners to create a tennis court, was now the main lawn. This left us with a steep south-facing slope down to the lawn and lesser slopes on the other sides of the old tennis court. These were all grassed and difficult to manage.

OPPOSITE The pond and surrounding terrace garden laid out by Molly Sanderson. In the far left corner is an *Abies georgei* and flanking the foreground steps are two laburnum trees.

My first planting of rhododendrons and azaleas on the western slope quickly showed signs of chlorosis from lack of iron in the soil, and I had to solve the problem before I could get cuttings rooted. The adjoining northern slope seemed the ideal site for a peat wall, about forty feet long and three feet at its highest point. It was easy to construct, just like building in stone or brick. Now twenty years old and still sturdily erect, it shows no signs of lateral seepage of lime, and the plants no symptoms of chlorosis. The rooted cuttings loved their new home. They romped through the wall, and within two or three years it was invisible under the cover of *Vaccinium* and *Gaultheria*, *Cornus canadensis* and the smaller *Rhododendron* species, including my favourite *R. williamsianum*, which is not only good in leaf but also beautiful in flower.

Hedges, we decided, were a great drain on our energies and resources. We had 1500 feet of them. Two particular examples of the problems we encountered with hedges spring to mind. In about 1965 we had planted two hundred Lawson cypress eight inches tall to replace an aged thorn hedge on the south and west boundaries. In five or six years we had adequate shelter. Over the next ten years we hardly noticed how tall it was growing until we realized that herbaceous plants nearby were dying from excessive shade. Stern measures were necessary: two young men with chain saws cut it down to five feet. There was no regrowth from the trunk, but remaining branches thickened out, and five years later we have quite a respectable hedge.

Another problem hedge was an ugly mixture of thorn, privet and brambles, infested with bishop's weed and bindweed. Ten years ago, in exasperation, the whole thing was removed to ground level and a long, interwoven fence was erected. The ground was covered with 500-gauge black polythene sheeting and weighed down with a two- or three-inch layer of large pebbles. The only plant to escape was *Fuchsia magellanica*

Spreading beneath a spindle tree is the double-flowered dwarf perennial poppy, appropriately named 'Fireball'. This beautiful 'ineradicable weed' came from County Kildare in the last century.

A flight of balustraded steps leading to the main lawn.

'Alba' which found a weak spot between the edging of the polythene and the wall. Thick, questing stems found another small hole, and as we couldn't get rid of it a piece has been allowed to remain.

About eighteen months later I explored below the stones and polythene, and to my surprise found a nice peaty texture of loam. I have since planted trees throughout the area – *Cupressus arizonica*, *Picea breweriana*, *Pinus pumila*, *Decaisnea fargesii*, *Vestia lycioides*, *Actinidia kolomikta*, and *Garrya elliptica* 'James Roof'; and, to my great delight, *Eucalyptus perriniana* has sown itself. The polythene and stones are still there, and the whole area looks good and is maintenance free.

In an effort to reduce maintenance of a steep slope from the house to the main lawn, we erected a strong concrete wall, infilled to level it up, and applied a good, thick layer of concrete surfacing. The whole area was balustraded and two wide flights of steps constructed. It has all weathered down nicely and has provided me with a south wall eight feet high. When small cracks appeared on the top surface they made useful homes for vigorous rock plants such as *Geranium pylzowianum* and *G. dalmaticum*,

Campanula poscharskyana and *C. portenschlagiana* and *Phuopsis stylosa*. The beautiful but invasive *Convolvulus sabatius* and *C. althaeoides* seem to be winter hardy on this site.

My gardening career has been a succession of love affairs with different genera. My first was with primroses. I started with the old double white, and became so besotted that I searched for years for all the old doubles and for the anomalous primroses – Jacks-in-the-green, hose-in-hose and the old *Primula juliae* hybrids. I found them almost embarrassingly easy to grow until the usual troubles of a monoculture arose – in this case vine weevils and root aphids. I still grow many primulas, but now work hard on a much broader base that includes the Auricula section and those from Asia. The old delight in them is still there.

I think it was rhododendrons that came next, but the number was limited by their special soil requirements. As interest in new genera arose for a few months or years, catalogues were scanned, nurseries searched and gardeners questioned. Willows supplanted *Sempervivum*, *Thalictrum* ousted *Mertensia*, *Gentiana* replaced *Hepatica* as the current object of my affection. It was not that old loves were cast off, just that new ones were added on! The result was that having worked through species of *Viola*, *Hosta*, *Bergenia*, *Geranium*, *Veratrum* (a small genus but difficult to acquire), *Eryngium*, *Trillium*, hardy orchids and many more, our garden was bursting at the seams.

The southern third of the garden was the little-used old kitchen garden, and I began to plan how to make use of it. I felt that the central square should be given over to a new rock garden. Luckily we had a source of basalt kerbstones, which we used to make curving pathways and walls, forming raised areas varying from six inches to two feet high. The soil was lightened by multitudinous lorry-loads of sharp sand, grit and peat and barrow-loads of our own garden compost. Only those who have had the opportunity of planting up a new rock garden can appreciate the excitement and deep contentment of the task, and the wonderful transformation achieved by the final dressing of pebbles. This was a successful experiment and the relief on our overcrowded areas was dramatic.

The periphery of the central square of the rock garden was mostly filled with small trees and shrubs, interplanted with *Helleborus*, *Trillium*, *Veratrum*, *Hosta*, *Eryngium*, *Bergenia*, *Meconopsis* and other herbaceous perennials. These in turn were underplanted with dwarf ferns, different forms of *Anemone nemorosa*, *Cyclamen hederifolium* in pink and white, *C. coum* for winter and *C. repandum* for spring. Early spring bulbs – *Scilla*, *Galanthus*, *Leucojum*, *Chionodoxa* – were thickly planted; by the time their foliage has died off the herbaceous plants have come through.

I must pay tribute to my most valuable helpmate in the garden (after Noel, of course) which is my garden apron. Originally bought about twenty years ago, it had been patched and mended till I could no longer use it. I was distraught – but I took it along to a ship's chandler and asked the elderly craftsman if he could make me another, but stronger. He gravely assured me that he could and in about ten days it was ready. The larger pockets were pouched and reinforced with rows of linen thread. I nearly embraced him with tears in my eyes!

The top tier of many small pockets carries pencils, labels, 'twistems', scissors, seed envelopes and a small notebook. Below the waist there are three pockets: one for a large hanky and garden twine; the middle is well-

ABOVE Ishlan, with *Hosta sieboldiana* and the giant groundsel (*Senecio smithii*) from the Falkland Islands in the foreground.

LEFT Molly Sanderson at work at Ishlan.

pouched and carries my secateurs and an old dinner knife; the left-hand one holds a small but strong trowel, a handfork and a small tube of antacid tablets – just in case.

The two large pockets at the bottom have a small but very efficient folding saw, a fern trowel, some lengths of nylon for temporary staking repairs – sometimes insect repellent wipes, and sometimes insecticide for use on soil or foliage. It *is* heavy but it is worth it, to avoid repeated return journeys uphill to the potting shed or tool house.

It was a surprise to me to realize one day that I was hooked on double flowers of all genera and species. *Primula modesta* has an enchanting little double form. There are many double-flowered *Anemone nemorosa*, blue, pink and white *Hepatica*, *Trillium grandiflorum*, *T. ovatum*, *Sanguinaria canadensis*, *Ranunculus aconitifolius*, *R. ficaria*, *R. acris* and many campanulas, especially the double white *Campanula persicifolia* with a green centre, many hardy geraniums, *Hesperis matronalis*, double white and pink *Polygonatum*, snow-drops, rockroses, even a hellebore – which sounds awful but is really rather fine. I know it is fashionable to despise double flowers as monstrosities, but I admire their perfect symmetry. As they do not have to rush into seed production their blooms last longer and we have more time to enjoy them.

Perhaps more valuable is the wide range of foliage variants, in gold, silver, bronze and purple. One of my favourite sights in the garden is the graceful tiers of *Cornus controversa* 'Variegata' silhouetted against the dense solid dark green of *Abies delavayi* var. *georgei*, with the golden Irish yew nearby. Just beyond is a five-year-old *Idesia polycarpa*, now ten to twelve feet high, whose widely tiered branches seem to mimic the *Cornus*, with large, cordate leaves that turn a soft peachy-cream colour in September.

We were lucky to have a natural spring in the garden, and we channelled the waters under the main lawn to the steep south slope, where I had great fun and hard work planning and building a series of small pools and cascades down to a soakaway. I discovered that water has a will of its own and does not always follow specially constructed inlets and outlets. In the end the system was made to work with only a minimum of leakage. This was to be my scree area, the south-facing incline giving full sun and perfect drainage, but *Androsace*, *Dionysia* and *Lewisia* did not take to it and had to be moved. On the whole it was the sturdier genera such as *Phlox*, *Dianthus*, *Gentiana*, *Geranium* and the New Zealand flora (which has always fascinated me, especially *Celmisia*) that eventually did well. To me, the greatest attraction of this area is the antics of the bird population, especially the blackbirds who paddle and flap and obviously enjoy the waterway as much as I do.

How does one summarize something as ephemeral as a garden? Both it and I have changed irrevocably over the thirty years since I began it. The Alpine Garden Society, which inspired my desire to be a *real* gardener, still holds my loyalty and affection, but there are so many other facets to gardening, all attractive to me. As Noel says, 'How can you summarize something which *has* no ending?'

Molly Sanderson

BEECH PARK
COUNTY DUBLIN

David Shackleton

I was born at Beech Park. I have lived here ever since, apart from my schooldays in England and the short period after my marriage, when I built a house of my own (having first built a walled garden). Five years later my mother died, and I moved back here.

The old walled garden, of one and a half acres, was by then overgrown, but I was fortunate that it was so near the house, because in those far-off

BELOW *Primula whitei*. Rare and much sought-after by collectors, it has been propagated by David Shackleton, who now has nearly three hundred plants.

The walled garden: vegetables retreat at the advance of the herbaceous borders.

days when it was first laid out, more than two centuries ago, walled gardens were often sited up to a mile away. Typical of its time, its main borders, lined with apple trees, were ranged down the centre and the four quarters were used for vegetables and soft fruit.

My first step was to remove most of the apple trees, leaving only a few to give us blossom and fruit. I also took out a small knot garden and the box hedges which bordered all the paths. Box is notorious for harbouring weeds and pests, and needs regular trimming: as I was going to have to rely on my own hard work and weedkillers in the future, this seemed a labour-saving move.

Apart from the conventional herbaceous borders, which are expanded every year at the expense of the vegetables and fruit, we grow many alpine plants in raised beds. Some of these beds are filled with a gritty mixture of soil, a little peat or leafmould, and chippings or lime rubble. This compost suits the majority of plants that require a limy soil. Others, the peat beds, are made up of three parts peat and one part fresh topsoil, with a balanced fertilizer raked in when planting. Each spring they are topdressed with this mixture.

Dwarf *Rhododendron* including *R. pemakoense*, 'Pipit' and the yellow 'Curlew' are among the many plants that thrive in the peat beds. The hardy orchids – *Dactylorhiza*, *Epipactis* and *Cypripedium* – flourish alongside diminutive irises such as *Iris cristata* and *I. verna*. In the shadier beds, *Arisaema candidissimum*, *Dryopteris wallichiana*, *Disporum oreganum*, *Trillium grandiflorum* 'Flore Pleno', *Primula whitei* and *P. gracilipes* are growing well.

New Zealand's mountain daisies (*Celmisia*) are particularly happy in our humid climate and enjoy the peaty mixture. Here we grow thirty-four different species ranging in size from *C. semicordata*, with large silver leaves, to the tiny *C. sessiliflora* 'Mount Potts'.

PREVIOUS PAGE A superb collection of herbaceous perennials, including blue *Iris*, *Symphytum* and *Geranium himalayense*.

The most successful herbaceous border is a hundred yards long. It faces north, getting no sun in winter, and is always moist in summer. These conditions suit *Phlox*, *Astilbe*, Asiatic *Primula*, five different *Ligularia* cultivars, *Roscoea*, hostas, ferns and many other plants, including ornamental grasses such as *Arundo*, *Stipa* and *Miscanthus*.

A number of blue Himalayan poppies also grow here. *Meconopsis betonicifolia* was crossed with *M. grandis* and the hybrid is known as *M × sheldonii*. Being a hybrid it varies, so that anyone who grows it can say that their form is the best. I have ended up with nine! Charles Nelson of the National Botanic Gardens and I judge them each year, and we have no doubt that the one known as 'Slieve Donard' is the finest.

One of the best phlox I have was given to my aunt by Edward Walpole, of Mount Usher gardens in Wicklow, nearly a hundred years ago. I used to call it 'Mount Usher Variety', then *Phlox maculata* 'Alba', but now I call it 'Miss Lingard', a name used in the United States. This is an early, long-flowering phlox with pure white flowers, and must surely have a wonderful constitution to have survived for so long in Irish gardens.

My aim has been to build up the most comprehensive collection of worthwhile hardy perennial plants within four walls, and to achieve this it has been necessary to visit the best private gardens and nurseries in these islands. The greatest fun for a keen gardener is to go round with a good plantsman discussing and looking at plants – always with a notebook to record the plants you must acquire for your own garden. This is one way to build up a collection, and you nearly always find gardeners are generous. Margery Fish was one such person. I remember the first time I visited her in Somerset. It took us five hours to inspect her three-quarter-acre garden. She was particularly fond of the plants that were grown in old cottage gardens, many of which would have been lost but for her enthusiasm. She gave me such good plants as the old double sweet rocket, several double primroses, the yellow snowdrop, her special *Astrantia* 'Shaggy' and the old double red wallflower called 'Bloody Warrior'.

Sadly, many of the plants I grow are reminders of donors who have long since died. Phylis Moore, wife of Sir Frederick Moore, one-time Keeper of the Botanic Gardens at Glasnevin, gave me a number of rare plants, and I am now sorry that in those days pocket recorders were not available to record the tales of the plants she grew. From her I obtained the dwarf form of *Astrantia carniolica*, and several rare snowdrops that had been given to her, in turn, by E. A. Bowles. Lady Moore was interested in old roses; she loved to take visitors by the arm and lead them to a magnificent specimen of 'Lady Hillingdon' which grew on the wall of her house saying, 'She is no good in a bed, best against a wall!'

My younger son Arthur, who has taken up gardening as a career, has built up a fine collection of old roses. He has also planted many interesting climbers on the fifteen-foot-high walls of the garden, and has trained them with the utmost skill.

The late Lord Talbot was one of my closest friends in more recent years. He was a collector by nature and introduced many interesting plants from the southern hemisphere, as he had a large estate in Tasmania. His untimely death was a severe blow to Irish horticulture. He gave me *Celmisia saxifraga* and *Blandfordia punicea*, a wonderful member of the lily family with waxy red bells – both are endemic in Tasmania.

The person who contributed most to my interest in alpine plants was Valerie Finnis, now Lady Scott. She introduced me to many good nurseries

Under the shade of a maidenhair tree (*Ginkgo biloba*) grows a profusion of summer-flowering perennials.

LEFT *Campanula* and dwarf *Phlox* have spread freely in this lichen-covered stone trough. A store of old earthenware pots – precious items these days – rests against the window of a shed.

BELOW LEFT A range of glass cloches in the greenhouse. The grey watering can between them was given to David Shackleton when he was ten.

A Campanula formanekiana, Saxifraga
'Tumbling Waters' *and a white* Lewisia
cotyledon *in the alpine house.*

and private gardens, and to her no door was closed. She is probably the most talented plantswoman and propagator I have had the privilege to meet. Her collection of Kabschia and Engleria saxifrages was second to none in Europe; I still grow many of those she gave me. Other excellent plants that have come my way were a superb scarlet form of *Anagallis*, *Phlox ensifolia* 'Nana', *Iris verna*, *Primula palinuri*, *Teucrium musimomum* and the pink bloodroot, *Sanguinaria canadensis* 'Rosea'.

Finally I would like to say that weeds are the greatest problem for gardeners – why grow them?

SHIEL

COUNTY DUBLIN

Mrs Olive Stanley-Clarke

When my gardening life began I knew nothing about gardening, and my ex-soldier husband, Kit, even less. Neighbours helped us to buy anemone corms and I had great difficulty deciding which side of the corm should be uppermost.

Then we thought of vegetables. I sowed parsley and lots of vegetable seeds. I put a label in the ground saying, 'Here parsley should come up'. It did – but not much else. Next we procured a gardener: a tall, venerable gentleman, slightly bent like overgrown asparagus, a permanent wet drip from his nose, and very gloomy. His name was Mr Frost. With his help we started a herbaceous border, and he said I must procure fish meal – unobtainable owing to the war. As we lived chiefly on fish, I scraped our plates daily and dug the skin and bones in. The dogs dug up the refuse – and the plants! Then we went on a wild spending spree and bought azaleas and rhododendrons, which were far more successful. We sawed military chests in half, filled them with soil, and grew some very good climbing shrubs in the sheltered courtyard.

Three years after the end of the Second World War we bought Earlscliff, a large ugly house nine miles from Dublin, looking over Killiney Bay. The garden was neglected and quite overrun with *Aubrieta* and a hideous mauve *Gladiolus*. I imagine we must have lived rather above our station in this large house, with two maids and a so-called gardener, and suddenly there was no money.

So we made the only intelligent decision we ever made and sold Earlscliff, keeping one field of about one and a half acres sloping down to the sea. This had the same stupendous view over the bay to the Wicklow Hills. With a lot of imagination, and ignoring the climate, it is reminiscent of the Bay of Naples. On this plot we planned to build a cottage and make a garden round it.

The first essential was shelter, and we were told to plant fast-growing poplars: bad advice, as they put up suckers, absorbing all the available moisture. The next important thing was to eliminate our view of the neighbours. I put bamboo stakes as markers at all vital points, to be replaced eventually by shrubs. Then I sat on the future site of the cottage and worked out a scheme. There would be a fiddle-shaped grass patch in the centre. My husband Kit took over this part, and did everything you should to make grass grow successfully. I scrounged old stones from Earlscliff for steps leading down from a flagged terrace in front of the cottage to the lawn. Herbaceous borders, nine feet wide, were laid out on each side of the lawn. A flagstone path leads to our field, which has flowering cherries that I dug up from Earlscliff – but I did it before showing the house to prospective buyers, so it wasn't cheating! There are camellias and tree peonies here and, at each side of the steps, we planted silver-green *Pittosporum*, a seedling japonica and an 'Albertine' climbing rose. We also put in a lovely *Cornus kousa*, an *Arbutus unedo*, varieties of *Euonymus*, *Magnolia grandiflora* 'Ferruginea', *Nandina domestica*, *Corokia × virgata*, *Sophora tetraptera*, and silver-leaved plants such as *Eucalyptus* and *Senecio*. Countless tree peonies have seeded wildly, and different colours come up every year. Heathers provide ground cover, and there are patches of blue delphiniums, with blue primulas in front, mauve and blue polyanthus and blue hydrangeas.

All the neighbours helped and shrubs were cheap, many coming from the Slieve Donard Nursery. We tried to plant all those that we loved best, often disagreeing between ourselves as to which these were. We have made hideous mistakes: in ignorance we planted much too closely, and I put a cedar in the lily of the valley bed, and a *Parrotia persica* on the edge of a narrow path.

The late Milo Talbot of Malahide Castle, County Dublin, was most

RIGHT Olive Stanley-Clark among the foliage of a *Pieris formosa* var. *forrestii*.

OVERLEAF: LEFT The lawn flows through the borders like a green river, past white foxgloves and the pineapple-scented Moroccan broom. In the far distance are Dublin Bay and the Wicklow Hills. Olive Stanley-Clarke will allow only white foxgloves to flourish: those of any other colour are instantly pulled out. RIGHT The blue stars of *Campanula* with golden *Potentilla* and a spray of the vivid rose 'Paul's Scarlet Climber'.

enthusiastic and helpful. One night after dinner he went out with a candle and matches (I couldn't find a torch) to see if a treasure had survived my treatment. And he took a *Gladiolus* from Shiel to the Royal Horticultural Society in London, where it won an award.

The garden is on rock, and two feet down there is yellow clay, more suitable for pottery than flowers, but we have a mild climate and little lime. I have had many casualties: *Lapageria rosea* does well on the back wall of the house, but I did something odd to the beautiful white-flowered one and I lost it, which nearly made me weep.

The bottle brushes, *Callistemon*, give me great joy, as do the large *Drimys winteri* var. *latifolia*, and the wonderful blue flowers of *Ceanothus* 'South-mead'. I almost died of pride when the *Irish Times* sent someone to photograph my white *Trillium*. But I cannot forgive Milo Talbot for planting *Vestia lycioides* underneath my bedroom window: it smells of tomcats and frustrates all my struggles to dig it out.

My gardening days are almost over. I am ninety. Fingers no longer do what I tell them to do, but I still love my wild garden, and every shrub and plant in it. There are excellent, sturdy weeds, with precious treasures in between, and I hope I shall be found dead one morning under my beautiful white tea tree.

Olive Stanley-Clarke

COOLCARRIGAN
COUNTY KILDARE

John Wilson-Wright

In Irish Coolcarrigan means 'corner of the hard ground' – very apt as the house and gardens are in the middle of several hundred acres of lime-rich pasture, surrounded on three sides by the soft and acid peat of the Bog of Allen. The flat, windswept landscape necessitated the planting of shelter-belts when my great-great-grandfather built the house in 1838. His son added more windbreaks, and also planted many specimen trees around the house. Greenhouses and garden walls were built, the main paths laid out, and a Victorian garden of laurels and conifers was planted, with some borders of annuals near the house.

In 1914 my grandmother inherited the house, and at my father's instigation more trees were planted, which improved the shape of the garden. During the unsettled years 1914–37 no work was done in the garden and it became overgrown with weedy shrubs, laurels and Monterey cypress. My mother, however, was keen on bulbs and planted large numbers after 1937. They are now a great feature of the place, and of the avenue leading to the house. Snowdrops and winter aconites precede the various crocuses and daffodils, and these are followed by carpets of bluebells, accompanied by pheasant's-eye narcissi which fill the air with their glorious scent. They have increased into large masses and are spectacular.

I inherited Coolcarrigan in 1972, and with my wife, Hilary, decided on some extensive clearing of the Monterey cypress which had by then reached fifty feet. 1973 saw us cutting, clearing and burning. Vistas were created. Our work was just completed when on 12 January 1974 the garden was hit by one of the most severe gales in recent years. The desolation the next morning was unbelievable: many good trees, exposed to the wind, had been tossed over. When the debris, branches, leaves and roots had been removed, large gaps were left, and we had to start planning all over again.

Fortune, however, was kind. One day soon afterwards I happened to be in England and called into Hillier's Garden Centre in Winchester,

Ancient vines, tomatoes and melons, pot plants, and a rose more than a hundred years old, all flourish in the warmth of this splendid glasshouse.

A path of querns, or mill-stones, has been laid between the peaches and nectarines that cover the walls in this glasshouse.

Hampshire, to make a few enquiries about plants and get some advice. A hurried telephone call was made; I was given directions, and soon found myself at Jermyns House, having a cup of tea and explaining my problems to the great plantsman himself, Sir Harold Hillier. We were joined by Roy Lancaster, and the two showed me round the Hillier Arboretum.

During that walk I was greatly inspired by what could be done with clever planting of interesting trees and shrubs, and much encouraged by the enthusiasm of my host, and impressed by his knowledge of his subject. Before I left I plucked up courage and asked him to come to Coolcarrigan, see my problem, and help me to remake the garden.

On Sir Harold's first visit rain did its best to wreck our precious time with the great man. Undaunted, umbrella aloft, and absolutely oblivious of his host's discomfort, he waded through the mud, presumably trying to visualize the garden we have today. Sir Harold proved to be a delightful guest, full of anecdotes about the interesting people he had met during his lifetime, and tales of his experiences during extensive travels abroad on plant-collecting expeditions. I owe him a tremendous debt of gratitude and I shall always remember his charm and his fantastic knowledge of plants.

While shrubs were being planted on Sir Harold's advice, Hilary planned colourful borders that can be seen from the windows of the house. A rose bed was planted with her favourite roses. 'Alexander', backed by the yellow foliage of a mature *Thuja plicata* 'Zebrina', is particularly successful. On the far side of the main lawn she made a late-flowering herbaceous

LEFT A mixed border backed by roses, broom, *Philadelphus* and the dark pillars of two large yews.

border, at its peak when most of the shrubs have finished flowering. Shrubs and trees form a background for the bed; these include the native strawberry tree, *Arbutus unedo*, which has lovely cinnamon-red bark, *Romneya coulteri*, and *Rosa moschata* growing over an old stump beside the gold of *Taxus baccata* 'Fastigiata Aureomarginata'.

Near the border stand the greenhouses. One contains peaches and nectarines. The other is divided into three sections, one inhabited by two old vines of green and black grapes; the middle section contains pot plants and a precious pink rose at least a hundred years old; the other is used for tomatoes, melons and freesias.

Hilary also designed a two-tier wall, built with stones rescued from an old cow house in the farmyard. Each level has been planted with a range of different rock plants that give good colour for most of the summer months.

In front of the house is a large *Cotoneaster congestus*, covered in summer by *Tropaeolum speciosum*, which provides a striking combination of scarlet and dark green. A path about a hundred yards long runs down the centre of the garden, with mixed shrubs on each side. Pairs of Doric columns that originally formed part of the portico of a large house, now sadly demolished, punctuate each end. Of constant interest are the reflections in the pond at the centre of the garden. Goldfish have to be guarded from a visiting heron.

Spring is probably the best time in this garden, but there is much of interest during the summer months. Trees and shrubs in a multitude of shades and shapes catch the eye. There are late-flowering shrubs, such as hydrangeas, and when autumn approaches leaves turn yellow, russet red and scarlet before disappearing until the next season. *Cercidiphyllum japonicum*, *Nyssa sylvatica* and *Acer palmatum* 'Osakazuki' all show their real value in the autumn.

A garden should also appeal to the nose, and with this in mind we have planted a scattering of *Mahonia* 'Charity', *Viburnum carlesii*, a selection of different cultivars of *Philadelphus* and, lastly, my favourite, *Magnolia wilsonii*.

One corner of the garden is a wild glade where a carpet of primroses and violets grows undisturbed under a light shade of oak. Their contrasting colours are delightful.

Part of the long avenue leading to the house is built on peat. In this area is an extensive collection of late-flowering *Rhododendron* hybrids growing against the green background of a wood of Norway spruce, edged by various whitebeams and rowan. These small trees give a wonderful variety of leaf shape and size, followed by magnificent autumn colour and lovely berries.

Coolcarrigan is an extensive garden, and no description of it could be written without a mention of our gardener, Patsy Prendergast, whose work has contributed so much to its beauty. It gives us great pleasure throughout most of the year, beginning with the early snowdrops at Christmas and ending with late autumn colour. One always has something new to look forward to.

ABOVE The rose 'Albertine' tumbling from a pergola. In the bed beneath are pink peonies, delphiniums, lupins, blue catmint (*Nepeta*) and lady's mantle (*Alchemilla mollis*).

GENERAL INDEX

INDEX OF PLANTS

INOCULATIONS

Most cats only see the vet once a year for the booster inoculation. At this annual visit, get the vet to check the cat over thoroughly; think of it as an annual health screen. Most illnesses, if spotted at an early stage, are treatable. Immunization is now available against many feline diseases, but diseases do vary from country to country, so check with your vet which vaccines are applicable to your cat.

Some cats, like humans, feel a little unwell after inoculations; they may even suffer from a stomach upset for a day or two, but this is no cause for worry unless it persists after forty-eight hours. The important thing is to give your cat as much protection as possible against feline diseases.

Your cat should have been inoculated before it comes to your house; if not, have this done as soon as possible. If you already have cats, keep the newcomer separated from the others until this has been done. Afterwards isolate the cat for seven days; it is possible for it to 'shed' virus for several days after inoculation.

As new diseases emerge, research vets and virologists try to isolate the viruses, and provide immunization against them. In recent years there has been considerable coverage by the popular press concerning feline leukaemia virus (FeLV) and feline immuno-deficiency virus (FIV), and calling these viruses 'feline AIDS'. This is a quite incorrect description and only serves to worry people unnecessarily. Other infections, such as feline infectious peritonitis (FIP) and chlamydia, are viruses that the veterinary profession are currently working on.

Various new vaccines have been, or are being, developed against some of these viruses, but not all have been approved for commercial use in every country, so availability varies. For current information, contact your veterinary surgeon.

RIGHT

By the age of twelve weeks, the kitten should have had a full course of inoculations.

⬥ FELINE INFECTIOUS ENTERITIS ⬥

DESCRIPTION/SYMPTOMS

This is a virus that attacks a widespread area, but particularly the bowels and the central nervous system. The symptoms of feline infectious enteritis (FIE) are many and varied; they may not all be present. Usually, the cat will have a hunched appearance, seem generally unwell, and may appear depressed. Vomiting, diarrhoea, and then dehydration will also be apparent.

ACTION

If your cat shows any of these signs, contact the vet as soon as possible, listing the symptoms; FIE is extremely infectious between cats, but does not live long outside a feline host. For this reason, the vet may prefer to make a home visit, rather than have the cat visit the surgery. If FIE is confirmed, there is little hope for recovery.

VACCINE

This is the single most important inoculation and is usually administered at ten to twelve weeks of age, followed by an annual booster. It is possible to inoculate against FIE and cat flu with a combined vaccine.

⬥ CAT FLU ⬥

DESCRIPTION/SYMPTOMS

This is a general term used to describe two viruses that affect the upper respiratory tract; feline calici virus (FCV) and feline viral rhinotracheitis (FVR), a herpes virus.

FCV may only cause snuffles and sneezes, but it can also create more serious problems such as ulceration, especially of the nose, mouth and tongue. FVR affects the nose, trachea and lungs, and can cause severe respiratory problems.

With both FCV and FVR, the cat will most typically be coughing and sneezing, with a runny discharge from eyes, nose and throat, and will show a loss of appetite.

ACTION

Cat flu is likely to be most serious in a kitten or an elderly cat and, if it is not treated immediately, can result in death. In an otherwise healthy adult, the symptoms are as severe but the cat has more stamina to recover. If the cat does recover, there is always the risk that they have become a carrier of the disease and may shed virus under stress, which could infect other cats. Any known carrier should be isolated, or taken to a home where there are no other cats that could be put at risk.

VACCINE

The combined vaccine for FCV, FVR and FIE is the most commonly used today, giving maximum available protection to your cat. It is a two-stage process, with the inoculations administered three weeks apart, usually starting at between nine and twelve weeks of age, depending on the particular vaccine used. Some brands are administered as a liquid squirted into the nostrils; these are usually live vaccines, and are not suitable for all cats. Your vet will advise you on the best vaccine for your cat or kitten.

• FELINE IMMUNO-DEFICIENCY VIRUS •

DESCRIPTION/SYMPTOMS

This is a virus that attacks the immune system, and is more similar in structure to the human counterpart HIV than FeLV (*see below*), but is still not transmissible between the two species. It also breaks down the immune system, but infected cats may enjoy long periods of good health before secondary infections become apparent.

ACTION

As with FeLV, the presence of feline immuno-deficiency virus (FIV) can be detected in the blood. If your vet feels that the cause of illness may be related to FIV, he will organize for blood tests to be carried out.

VACCINE

Much research is being carried out, and it is hoped that an inoculation for FIV will be available soon.

• FELINE LEUKAEMIA VIRUS •

DESCRIPTION/SYMPTOMS

This is currently one of the most controversial diseases, as it is often, mistakenly, referred to as feline AIDS. It is true to say that there are similarities between feline leukaemia virus (FeLV) and human immuno-deficiency virus (HIV); the FeLV virus breaks down the cat's immune system, and is transmitted by prolonged exposure to an infected cat's saliva and/or blood, usually while mating. For this reason, many owners of stud cats insist on a recent FeLV test for any visiting queens.

In certain ways, the chemical structure of the two viruses are similar; indeed, some of the early inroads into finding an antibody to HIV were achieved by examining the FeLV virus, as more was known about it than AIDS. Here the similarities stop and it must be made clear that the two viruses are not interactive or transmissible.

ACTION

The symptoms for FeLV vary because of the nature of the virus. A cat does not die of FeLV, but of whatever illness it develops due to the breakdown of its immune system. Persistent infections will probably cause your vet to investigate further, and a simple blood test will reveal whether or not the virus is present. If the test proves positive, the cat will be retested a fortnight or so later. It is quite possible for a cat to register positive, indicating that it has had recent contact with the virus, then after a fortnight, to register negative, showing only a transient FeLV infection.

As research continues on the FeLV virus it is important to talk to your vet, who will be able to give you all the recent information. Remember that it is not a death sentence for your cat if it proves to be positive; however, if you have other cats that are negative it would be sensible to rehome it to a cat-free household, where it will probably live on to advanced years, but without the possibility of infecting other cats. Like most viruses, FeLV cannot live for long outside a feline host and is killed by most disinfectants.

VACCINE

Although a FeLV vaccine has been available in the USA, it is only since the beginning of 1992 that a vaccine has been licensed for use in the UK. Vaccination is a two-stage process with inoculations administered fifteen to twenty-one days apart. It is advised that only healthy FeLV-negative cats should be inoculated and before inoculation your cat should be tested to be sure that it is negative. FeLV-negative queens should be inoculated before mating; pregnant cats should *not* be inoculated.

You cannot catch AIDS from a cat that is FeLV positive any more than your cat could acquire AIDS from a person who is HIV positive.

• RABIES •

DESCRIPTION/SYMPTOMS

This is one of the killer diseases and, unlike most animal infections, is transmissible to man — often with fatal consequences. For this reason, all rabies-free countries enforce a quarantine period for the import of livestock from territories where the disease exists. Hydrophobia is the clinical name for rabies, and describes the ultimate symptom – fear of water. A change in temperament is often the first sign; a usually quiet and docile cat may suddenly, without provocation, become aggressive. It may foam at the mouth and in later stages suffer from paralysis, especially of the jaw.

ACTION

Once an animal has contracted rabies, there is little that can be done for it. If rabies is suspected, it is imperative to contact your vet for a confirmed diagnosis; the local authority and the police will have to be notified. The disease is transmitted by saliva and other body fluids, which contain a high concentration of the virus. This means that a simple lick from an infected animal into a small open wound on a human poses just as much risk of transferring the infection as an actual bite from the animal.

VACCINE

Most countries with endemic rabies insist that all animals capable of carrying the disease are immunized against it. There are certain island nations, for example the UK and New Zealand, which are rabies-free zones at present. In the UK, the government policy is not to inoculate against rabies, except for animals that are to be exported, although this could well change with the opening of the Channel Tunnel.

• FELINE INFECTIOUS PERITONITIS •

DESCRIPTION/SYMPTOMS

When the feline infectious peritonitis (FIP) virus was first discovered, it caused widespread anxiety. It is extremely difficult to diagnose, because of the variety of associated symptoms, and a positive diagnosis can usually only be made from a post-mortem; by this time it is somewhat late to help the poor cat. At first, it was thought to be highly infectious and it put terror in the heart of many a cat breeder.

There appear to be two kinds of FIP, wet and dry. Classic FIP manifests itself by way of a swollen abdomen as the peritoneum (the membrane lining the cavity of the abdomen) fills with fluid. This is accompanied by general ill health, diarrhoea, vomiting and weight loss. The dry form affects the nervous system and is usually harder to detect as the symptoms are similar to those of many other ailments. These include jaundice, respiratory problems, loss of coordination and, in the final stages, fits.

ACTION

Recent research shows that FIP is not as infectious as was first thought. FIP is one of many corona viruses; although it is possible to take a blood test and establish the titre level (concentration) of these viruses in the blood, it does not give much information as to which particular corona virus the cat has been exposed to. It is important that no cat is put down simply on the result of a positive corona virus (titre) blood test. It is now thought that FIP is mainly carried in an infected cat's saliva; it cannot live long outside the feline host and is killed by most veterinary disinfectants.

VACCINE

To date, there is no inoculation available for FIP but, as veterinary science progresses every day, there may well be a vaccination available soon.

• CHLAMYDIA •

DESCRIPTION/SYMPTOMS

Only recently has chlamydia been isolated as a distinct virus. The symptoms can be very similar to those of severe cases of cat flu – usually severe discharges from the eyes and nose. It is not a common infection, and is generally found in multi-cat breeding households.

ACTION

Take the cat to the vet for the correct diagnosis. If it is chlamydia he will administer a course of antibiotics. It is important to keep the cat's eyes moist to prevent adhesions forming between the inner eyelid and cornea and the vet will prescribe a suitable medication. If the cat is part of a multi-cat household, it will have to be isolated.

VACCINE

In the UK, a vaccine has been developed, and has been licensed for administration by veterinary surgeons since 1991.

PARASITES

T here are two main kinds of parasitic infestation: internal and external. Both cause distress and discomfort and, if left untreated, can result in illness. The earlier the signs of infestation are spotted, the sooner they can be treated. If you suspect any of the following may be present in your cat, take it to the vet as soon as possible.

INTERNAL PARASITES

• WORMS •

DESCRIPTION/SYMPTOMS

At some time during its life, almost every cat gets worms. There are two kinds: roundworms and tapeworms. They can be avoided by worming the cat regularly; suitable preparations can be bought from the vet.

Roundworms live in the intestine, feeding on partly digested food. This means that the cat is not receiving all the necessary nutrients from its diet, and will look out of condition with a dull, starey coat, and may have a pot-bellied appearance. In a young kitten, the results can be more dramatic than simple loss of condition: diarrhoea, constipation and anaemia may well occur, making the cat seriously ill. The roundworm's eggs are passed out in the faeces, and can lead to re-infestation without attention to hygiene.

Tapeworm infection is usually identified by the presence of what look like wriggly grains of rice around the anus; these are the ripe sections of the tapeworm containing the egg. Fleas act as an intermediate host in the tapeworm's life cycle: the flea eats the egg, the cat eats the flea, and the egg is released into the intestine for a new cycle to begin. For this reason it is also important to deflea your cat.

ACTION

It is possible to 'worm' your cat for both varieties with one pill, but this may not be suitable in all cases. Your vet will advise you of the most appropriate preparation, the dose to be given and the frequency with which the course should be repeated. If you do buy a preparation from a shop, make sure you read the instructions clearly before administering to your cat. However, proprietary brands are rarely as effective as those the vet can supply on prescription.

• TOXOPLASMOSIS •

DESCRIPTION/SYMPTOMS

Although not strictly a parasitic infection, this condition causes much publicity and concern. It is a protozoal zoonosis, which means that it is a disease communicable to humans from animals, particularly, in this case, from cats and dogs.

ACTION

Toxoplasmosis rarely causes illness in cats, or indeed in adult humans. The real risk is to the unborn human embryo where, in extreme cases, it could cause a deformity such as blindness. The eggs from toxoplasmosis are excreted in concentration in the faeces of infected cats; for this reason it is important for pregnant women to avoid handling litter trays. Likewise, ensure that children wash their hands after handling the cat and especially after performing litter tray duties.

EXTERNAL PARASITES

A ny cat allowed to go outside will meet with an assortment of external parasites all dying to get stuck into a feline host.

BELOW
The most obvious reason for a cat to scratch is simply to relieve an itch, as this cat is demonstrating. However, if a cat persistently scratches it could be indicative of flea infestation and so it would be sensible to consult the vet so the appropriate treatment can be administered.

• FLEAS •

DESCRIPTION/SYMPTOMS

Fleas are the most common parasite. Found on town and country cats, they are a universal pest.

Usually, the first sign of flea infestation is that the cat starts to scratch a lot, particularly around the back of its head and at the base of the spine. This is most common in the spring and summer, when the warmer weather encourages the fleas to come out of winter hibernation. Unless your cat has a severe infestation, you may not actually see the fleas – they hop very quickly – but it is easy to detect if your cat is infested by examining the fur for the telltale sign of flea dirt, which looks like little black specks similar to coarse-ground black pepper. Fleas are blood suckers and, although their dirt looks black, it is actually digested blood. Put the cat on a clean, white surface that has been dampened and comb through the cat's fur; if the dirt that falls out turns red when it dissolves on the damp surface this is a sure sign of fleas.

ACTION

It is possible to buy flea collars, but they are rarely effective and can sometimes cause an allergic reaction around the neck. Flea powders and sprays bought from a store are usually equally ineffective; go to the vet and buy a good-quality product which will effectively rid your cat of these pests. It is also possible to buy a preparation for treating your home and furnishings. Always read and follow the instructions correctly.

Regular spraying of your cat and its bedding, especially during the summer, should ensure that fleas do not become an endemic problem in your home. For every flea on a cat, there can be 200 living in the house waiting their turn to jump on the cat, feed, hop off, breed and multiply. Remember that fleas are quite partial to human blood too, but will only stay long enough to have a quick bite; we do not have the invitingly furry bodies that encourage fleas to take up permanent residence.

• MITES •

DESCRIPTION/SYMPTOMS

There are basically two kinds of mites: those that attack the fur, and those that live in the ears. Mites themselves are, as their name implies, minute and cannot be detected by the human eye; it is the damage they cause that can be clearly seen.

Fur mites can cause hair loss, resulting in the scaly, scabby skin condition that is often called 'mange'. An unpleasant thick, brown, waxy, pungent build-up in the ear canal is typical of ear mite infestation.

ACTION

Mange can look quite similar to ringworm, so the cat should be taken to the vet for correct diagnosis and treatment. For ear mites, you can gently clean the outer area of the ear with a cotton wool swab or cotton bud, but extreme caution must be used as the ear is easily damaged. Your vet will have to see the cat to prescribe the right kind of ear drops, so it is best to leave the cleaning to him, too.

• TICKS •

DESCRIPTION/SYMPTOMS

Ticks are usually found on cats that live in the countryside, where they pick them up from farm animals or long grass.

Like fleas, ticks are blood suckers; however, rather than hopping from one cat to another, the tick buries its head deep into the host's skin, where it remains until it has drunk its fill or is physically removed. A well-fed tick, bloated with blood, can easily be the size of a pea.

ACTION

It is quite easy to remove a tick yourself; the important thing is to make sure that you get the whole tick out, head and all. If the head is left behind in the skin, it will become infected and cause an abscess to develop. The tick has hooks on its head which it uses to attach itself to its host; to get these hooks to relax it will be necessary to anaesthetize the tick with alcohol. If you do not have surgical alcohol handy, use vodka, whisky or gin – more expensive but just as effective. Swab the tick with alcohol and then pull it out with a pair of tweezers. This can be a bit gruesome so, if you are squeamish, take the cat to the vet for him to deal with it.

BELOW *will make a detailed*
If ear mite infestation inspection of the ear
is suspected, the vet canal.

Inevitably, at some time during your cat's life you will have to administer a pill to it. Cats do tend to wriggle, but with a little practice it is not too difficult a task. It is most important, especially if the pill is part of a course of antibiotics, that you ensure the whole pill has been taken.

HIDING THE PILL

You can try concealing a pill in food so the cat takes the medication without realizing it. Do not crush it up and mix it in the cat's meal as some of the food and pill may remain uneaten. Use a small piece of favourite food, such as minced chicken or fish, crush the pill and mix the two together to something the size of a walnut. Make sure the cat eats it all, and you will know that it has also taken the medication. Many cats love butter: again, crush the pill and mix it with a small amount of soft butter; put on the top of one of the cat's paws and you will find it will lick it all off.

GIVING A PILL BY HAND

The obvious way is to open the cat's mouth and put in the pill, but this is not as easy as it sounds. Some cats are extremely clever at hiding pills in their mouths, then spitting them out when you are not looking. With practice, the following method is the simplest:

1 To open the mouth, place your hand over the cat's jaw, holding the head back; with thumb and forefinger on either side, push on the cheeks and the mouth will open.

2 With your other hand, quickly shoot the pill as far back in the throat as possible.

3 Shut the mouth, and keep it closed with one hand, while closing the nostrils with the other – this forces the cat to swallow. When you have seen the cat swallow, release your hands. The pill has been administered.

PILL POPPERS

It is possible to buy a gadget known as a 'pill popper' (see above). This is a long plastic plunger which looks a bit like a cake icing syringe. Load the pill, open the cat's mouth, insert the popper, and push the plunger. This shoots the pill to the back of the cat's mouth. Close the mouth and nostrils as in the method described right.

AILMENTS AND ILLNESSES

In general, the feline species is a healthy one. Your cat, regularly inoculated, well fed and cared for, should live a good life. However, there are various infections to which it may succumb. Most of these can be cleared up quickly and effectively by correct diagnosis and the administration of antibiotics from a qualified veterinary surgeon; some can be quite effectively treated at home. It is always best to seek veterinary advice, even if only over the telephone. The golden rule is never attempt any treatment unless you are completely confident that you are carrying out the correct procedure in the right way.

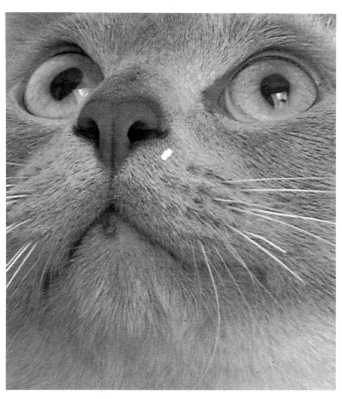

• ABSCESSES •

DESCRIPTION

An abscess is most likely to form following a bite from another cat, but this is not always the case. Any untreated puncture to the skin can become infected, causing an abscess. Diagnosis is not difficult; an abscess looks very much like a large pimple which, in effect, is what it is – a pus-filled lump sited at the point of the wound.

ACTION

It is important to clear the infection as soon as possible to prevent septicaemia setting in; the cat should be given a course of antibiotics immediately. Applying a hot compress will help to burst the abscess and evacuate the pus. Afterwards, the open wound must be kept clean to stop the abscess reforming; applying a wad of cotton wool soaked in warm, dilute, saline solution is effective.

• ACNE •

DESCRIPTION

Feline acne is most commonly seen on the chin of a cat that lives in a single-cat household. It is not easy for a cat to reach this part of its face. Without the aid of a feline friend's rasping tongue to clean away the greasy remains of a meal, the pores are likely to clog up, forming blackheads. These may become infected and cause acne which, if severe, can result in an abscess (*see left*).

ACTION

The application of cotton wool soaked in warm saline solution will help the acne to come to a head and burst; follow up by applying a mild antiseptic suitable for cats. If the condition persists, contact your vet; it responds well to antibiotics.

• ANAL GLANDS •

DESCRIPTION

On either side of the anus are two small openings which lead directly from the anal glands. Because of their situation, it is possible for these openings to become blocked, causing an infection to set in in the glands. Normally, these openings are almost imperceptible; when blocked they are more obvious and look like two black grains of rice on either side of the anal sphincter. The cat may drag its bottom along the ground, or indulge in frequent washing of the area, obviously trying to relieve an irritation.

ACTION

The blockages can be removed, with care and in a very docile cat, by quickly pulling them out with fingers or a pair of tweezers. This should never be attempted with a strange cat, or if you do not know what you are doing. Treatment of infected anal glands is best left to your vet, but it is possible to express them yourself. Apply a hot cotton wool compress and gently squeeze from each side. The exuding matter will smell pungent and, if you do not have a strong stomach, the process is best left for the vet to carry out. Untreated, the infection may result in an abscess which, in this sensitive area, is extremely uncomfortable for a cat.

• ANAL PROLAPSE •

DESCRIPTION

This is not particularly common, but once seen is never forgotten; it looks dramatic, and will cause many owners to go into a panic. Anal prolapse is when a small section of bowel turns inside out, with the result that the cat looks as if it has a raspberry protruding from its back passage.

ACTION

It is important to get the cat to the vet as soon as possible as it will be in great discomfort, and may well need surgical attention. The main cause of anal prolapse is an unbalanced diet without adequate roughage, although there are other reasons. Your vet will advise you. Never attempt to push the bowel back into the rectum yourself.

• ARTHRITIS •

DESCRIPTION

This is most common in the older cat but, as with human arthritis, it can strike at any age. In younger cats, it can be related to calici virus, one of the forms of cat flu, and is usually transient. Arthritis affects the skeletal joints, resulting in swelling, inflammation, pain and (if in a limb joint) lameness.

ACTION

Contact your vet for a correct diagnosis, and discuss which of the treatments currently available are most suited to your cat. Heat is a great soother, and a hot water bottle or heated pad will give much relief to this painful complaint. Massage is often beneficial, but should be administered with care; there are many electric massagers available commercially. Applied correctly, these can alleviate some of the pain and increase mobility in the affected limb. Osteopathic manipulation is sometimes used. Arthritis can be encouraged by obesity, so it is a good idea to keep your cat at the right weight for its size and build.

LEFT
Any cat suffering from arthritis will benefit from additional heat, and a heated cat bed will help tremendously.

• ASTHMA •

DESCRIPTION

Cats can show allergic reactions to many environmental agents, and these cause the respiratory distress commonly called asthma. The symptoms can be snuffles, sneezes, weeping eyes and difficulty in breathing, but these could equally be indicative of cat flu.

ACTION

It is important that your vet examines the cat to make the correct diagnosis. If he thinks asthma is the cause, he may suggest that the cat is confined indoors, with the windows closed, when the pollen count is high.

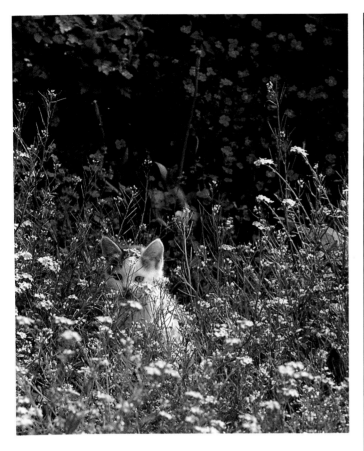

ABOVE
Just like humans, cats can suffer from allergies such as asthma and hay fever. If your cat is prone to this, it is wise to keep it confined indoors when the pollen count is high.

BELOW
If an allergic reaction causes irritation to the eyes, the vet may well suggest the application of a soothing eye ointment; never administer a preparation that is not recommended by the vet.

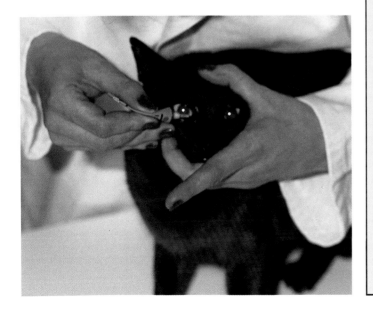

• CONSTIPATION •

DESCRIPTION

Constipation is usually caused by an unbalanced diet, and so can quite often be cured by adding roughage to the food, such as bran. A constipated cat will typically have an 'open' (out of condition) coat, appear lethargic and will strain on its litter tray without passing a motion. The occasional hard stool may be blood-spotted, caused by a ruptured capillary.

ACTION

A constipated cat may be treated at home by giving it a little liquid paraffin. If symptoms persist, consult your vet as there may be a more serious underlying cause, such as an intestinal blockage caused by fur balls.

• DANDRUFF •

DESCRIPTION

This is not a life-threatening problem, but does look unsightly. Dead flakes of skin, or dander, build up in the fur and tend to accumulate if the cat is not regularly groomed. Dry skin can aggravate the situation, and this may be caused by diet, so a change to a more oily food such as sardines or pilchards may help to clear it.

ACTION

An application of fur-conditioning lotion will give a rapid, but temporary, improvement. If the condition persists, there may be a dermatological problem for which your vet will be able to prescribe suitable treatment. Also consult your vet if you find yourself with a skin rash on your chest or arms, as this may be an indication of skin mite infection transferred from the cat.

• DIABETES •

DESCRIPTION

This can affect a cat at any age, but is usually seen in older or overweight animals. The symptoms are an increase in thirst and appetite, but with marked loss of weight. Your vet can make a confirmed diagnosis of this condition after blood and urine samples have been analyzed.

ACTION

Treatment of diabetes, as with humans, is with daily injections of insulin; your vet will show you how to do this and, once you have mastered the technique, it is not difficult. It is important that a diabetic cat receives meals at regular intervals, and that the diet should not contain carbohydrates or sugar. Once the treatment has begun and the condition stabilized, there is no reason why the cat should not live for many years providing the correct medication and modified diet are followed.

• DIARRHOEA •

DESCRIPTION

Many cats have the occasional loose motion. In most cases, this is caused by eating something too rich, or perhaps not as fresh as it should have been.

ACTION

Starve the cat for twenty-four hours, giving it only still mineral (not tap) water to drink, and a teaspoon of plain, live yoghurt three times a day. This will help to readjust the natural bacterial balance in the intestine. If the diarrhoea persists for more than forty-eight hours, or the condition worsens, seek the advice of your vet.

• EAR PROBLEMS •

DESCRIPTION

If a cat starts to scratch its ears, or holds its head to one side, there is probably an ear problem. The most common cause is ear mites (see 'Parasites'), but it could be that a foreign body has entered the ear canal, such as a grass seed, which, if it germinates, will cause extreme irritation and discomfort.

ACTION

Seek veterinary advice for correct diagnosis and treatment.

• ECZEMA •

DESCRIPTION

The problem with eczema is that, although it can have many different causes, the outward manifestations of the disease are the same, which makes diagnosis and treatment difficult.

ACTION

Flea allergy is the most common cause of eczema, and the treatment for this is obviously a good dose of flea spray, and regular spraying of the house to ensure that fleas do not continue to breed. Miliary eczema may be caused by a hormone imbalance, often caused by a female kitten being spayed at too young an age for the endocrine system to have fully developed. If this is the case, the cat will be treated with hormone replacement. Certain foodstuffs, just as with humans, can cause an allergic eczema, and this can be treated by a change in diet. Any hair loss with accompanying bald, scaly patches should be investigated by the vet as it could be ringworm (see 'Parasites'), which is highly contagious.

LEFT
An example of flea allergy (dermatitis). The area has been shaved; it would normally show sparse broken hairs.

• FELINE DYSAUTONOMIA •

DESCRIPTION

This is a relatively recent discovery, originally known as Key-Gaskell syndrome. As one of the main symptoms is a dilated pupil, in one or both eyes, it has also been called dilated pupil syndrome. Other symptoms may include vomiting, constipation, along with dryness of the nose and mouth causing gagging and difficulty in eating.

ACTION

Research still continues into this condition. At present it is not known how contagious it is, how it is transmitted or how it is caused. Treatment can, therefore, only be symptomatic. It usually affects younger cats, although it has occasionally been seen in older animals, and it has a high mortality rate.

• FELINE INFECTIOUS ANAEMIA •

DESCRIPTION

For some reason feline infectious anaemia (FIA) seems particularly to affect young male cats. It is a bacterial infection and is thought to be transmitted by flies and mosquitoes. Symptoms include lethargy and loss of appetite, and those normally pink-coloured areas such as the lips, gums and mouth will be noticeably pale.

ACTION

The disease can be confirmed by blood analysis and, if this is the case, further tests for FELV will be carried out. If only FIA is present, and is diagnosed at an early stage, it is treatable; if it is combined with FELV the prognosis is not so optimistic.

FITS

DESCRIPTION

You will be in little doubt if your cat is having a fit; it will fall over, salivate and probably twitch.

ACTION

This requires immediate veterinary assistance, as a fit can have many causes, all of which require immediate attention. If you suspect that your cat has swallowed some form of toxic poison, act quickly. Make up a strong solution of salt and water. Force it down the cat's throat to make it sick; this will get rid of as much poison as possible from the stomach before it becomes ingested. *Never* induce vomiting if a caustic substance is the suspected poison. If you have to handle a cat while it is having a fit, protect yourself with thick gloves and wrap the cat in a towel or blanket.

BELOW

If your cat suffers a fit, protect yourself by wearing thick gloves and wrap the cat up firmly in a blanket.

• FUR BALLS •

DESCRIPTION

Cats are very clean creatures and spend much of their time in personal and social grooming. This leads to a certain amount of fur being swallowed. Fur is indigestible and, if quantities are allowed to build up in the intestines, a blockage known as a 'fur ball' will result. Fur balls will probably make the cat cough and may well cause discomfort and constipation.

ACTION

In the wild, a cat would rid itself of fur balls by eating grass, which acts as a natural emetic. Modern housebound cats may need to have hair balls expelled with a dose of liquid paraffin – in an adult one teaspoon, twice a day, for three days, and less for a kitten. The prevention is to groom your cat regularly with a brush and comb, so there is less fur to be swallowed.

HAEMATOMA

DESCRIPTION

A haematoma looks very much like an abscess (a large fluid-filled swelling), but a haematoma is filled with blood and not pus. It is usually seen on the ear, often as the result of a cat fight.

ACTION

The ear is a delicate organ and, if this condition is left untreated, can result in a permanent 'flop' ear. The cat should be seen by the vet as soon as possible if this is to be prevented, and it will also need a course of antibiotics to stop infection setting in.

TOP

A haematoma – a large blood-filled swelling – is usually seen on the ear and is frequently caused by cat fights.

ABOVE

If the haematoma is left untreated the ear will develop a deformity known as flop ear. Immediate veterinary treatment will prevent this.

• MOUTH PROBLEMS •

DESCRIPTION

Usually the first indication that the cat has a problem with its mouth is when it starts to claw at its face or seems interested in food but is unwilling to eat.

For a kitten of around sixteen weeks of age, this is most likely to be part of the teething process. As the adult teeth develop, they push the first teeth out, which can cause the gums to become sore. Occasionally, an adult tooth will not come down straight, resulting in two teeth appearing side by side.

There may be other reasons your cat's mouth is painful. It may have a foreign body stuck in its throat, such as a splinter of bone, a needle, or some other sharp object. Gum disorders, such as gingivitis (inflammation of the gums), will cause severe discomfort, as will a loose tooth. Although these conditions are most common in older cats, they can happen at any age, especially if the cat has not been provided with something crunchy in its diet to adequately exercise the teeth and gums.

ACTION

If your kitten suffers severe teething pain, consult your vet; gum salves manufactured for human babies should never be used.

It you suspect your cat has a foreign body stuck in its throat, contact the vet immediately. The blockage will need to be removed as soon as possible to prevent the cat choking.

For gum disorders and loose teeth, a veterinary examination will be needed and, where necessary, teeth will be extracted.

ABOVE
There are several minor gum and teeth disorders that can be treated easily. However, more serious illnesses may be indicated following an inspection of the mouth. For example, paleness in the gums can be indicative of anaemia, possibly feline infectious anaemia (FIA).

• RINGWORM •

DESCRIPTION

This is a very misleading name, as ringworm has nothing to do with worms, parasitic or otherwise. It is an extremely contagious fungal infection, which needs prompt diagnosis to prevent it spreading further, and immediate, often prolonged, veterinary treatment.

The symptoms vary and not all may be present; they are, usually, loss of fur – which tends to break rather than fall out – associated bald spots and sometimes scaly patches on the skin. Head, ears and toes are the most common sites. However, any hair loss should be treated as suspect and the affected cat should be taken to the vet for examination. Diagnosis can be difficult; in most cases ringworm will fluoresce under an ultraviolet Wood's lamp, but not always – some forms of ringworm can only be detected from a culture grown from a skin scraping.

ABOVE
Ringworm affects mostly the head, ears and feet, but in severe cases can occur anywhere on the body.

ACTION

Once diagnosed, ringworm is usually treated with Griseofulvin; it may also be necessary to use a fungicidal shampoo. Griseofulvin works by getting into the blood stream and working its way into each individual hair, killing the fungus as it goes. In order to speed up the treatment, some vets clip the fur of longhaired cats – the quicker the Griseofulvin can get to the tip of the hair, the sooner the fungus is cleared out of the system. Some vets also clip the whiskers of shorthaired cats; these are much longer than the close-lying, short fur, and by washing its face the cat could easily reinfect hair that is otherwise clear of ringworm.

An infected cat should be isolated from others in the household and it should be kept indoors to prevent infection of neighbouring cats. A strict code of hygiene should be followed: burn all bedding and replace it, following your vet's advice for laundering of the new bedding. As ringworm is one of the few conditions transferable between cats and humans, keep a close eye on you and your family for the formation of scaly, itchy patches; the treatment will be the same, but you will need to contact your doctor for it. Do not allow your doctor to persuade you to put down your cat because you have ringworm – nobody has ever died of ringworm.

After four to six weeks, the vet will want to re-examine the cat under the Wood's lamp, to make sure that all traces of ringworm have been eliminated; if not, a further course of Griseofulvin will be administered. Until your household is cleared, it is inadvisable to visit friends with animals of their own, or for them to visit you, as ringworm can spread on shoes and clothing.

ACCIDENTS AND EMERGENCIES

Accidents happen, even in the most caring homes, and it is best to know what to do in the event of an emergency. A knowledge of feline first aid could make the difference between life and death to your cat. However, if you try to administer first aid, and are not sure of the correct procedure, you could do more harm than good. The chapter on *'Safekeeping of Cats'* lists some of the potentially dangerous situations your cat may get into; here we give you basic advice on the immediate actions you can take to help your cat if an accident happens.

◊ GET TO THE VET ◊

For all, bar minor injuries that can be treated at home, apply immediate first aid, if you are confident on the procedure, and then take your cat to the vet immediately. Calling the vet to your home only wastes time, and the chances are that whatever emergency treatment is needed, and this may be an operation, will be available only at the surgery.

If you have to drive the cat to the vet, do not travel alone. If possible, get a friend or neighbour to go with you. Left unrestrained in a carrier, the injured cat may panic and damage itself further. It is better to wrap the cat in a blanket and for someone to cuddle it; this reassures the cat and makes it less likely to go into shock. Also, you are less liable to have a road accident if you know the cat is securely held and as comfortable as possible.

After any accident, it is important to treat the cat for *shock*: keep the cat quiet and warm – wrap it in a towel or blanket – until you can get to the vet's surgery.

LEFT
Cats exerting their territorial rights are quite likely to fight; look out for any sign of a puncture wound, as this could easily lead to infection and the formation of an abscess.

• ANIMAL BITES •
(*SEE ALSO* **SNAKE BITES**)

INDICATIONS	ACTION
Any free-ranging cat will, inevitably, get into a scrap with another cat at some point. The mouths of all animals, including humans, contain many bacteria which, once in the bloodstream, can cause infections.	• Immediately bathe any wound with a diluted antiseptic suitable for cats, to minimize local infection; even a small puncture wound can result in an abscess. • Next, contact the vet who will give an antibiotic injection immediately, and prescribe the relevant follow-up course of antibiotic pills.

• BURNS •

INDICATIONS	ACTION
There are basically three kinds of burn, all of which will result in blistering of the affected part: • Contact burns, from direct contact with a hot surface. • Scalds caused by contact with boiling liquid. • Caustic burns from contact with toxic chemicals. The most likely place for a cat to suffer the first two is in the kitchen. Caustic burns occur more often if a cat wanders into an area where dangerous chemicals are stored.	• Immediately hold the blistered area under cold running water. • *Never* administer ointments, lotions or butter to the burn. • Do not puncture blisters. • Get the cat to the vet as soon as possible.

RIGHT
If your cat has suffered a burn, immediately hold the blistered area under cold running water until the injury has cooled completely.

❁ RESUSCITATION ❁

Immediate resuscitation is vital if your cat stops breathing. This can be due to several causes, most commonly *drowning (which includes new-born kittens that have inhaled amniotic fluid) and electric shock (see overleaf).*

1 Tilt back the cat's head, hold the mouth shut, and blow into both nostrils.

2 Wait until air is expelled and repeat until the cat starts breathing on its own. If the cat still does not breathe, heart massage is needed.

3 For heart massage, lay the cat on its side and rapidly press and then release the area of the chest behind the elbow where the heart is situated. Do not worry how firm you are in treating the cat; if it is not breathing it is, to all intents and purposes, dead. If you manage to revive your cat and it lives, a broken rib is the least of your worries.

• DROWNING •

INDICATIONS

A cat does not have to fall into a deep lake to drown; drowning takes place when the lungs become full of water instead of air, and can be caused in many ways. The urgency is to expel this water from the lungs so that the cat can breathe again.

ACTION

● Hold the cat with its head pointing downward and slap its back firmly. If water is not expelled, and the cat appears not to be breathing, drastic action is called for.
● Grasp the cat firmly by the scruff of its neck and by the rear legs, and swing it firmly downwards.
● Once the water has been expelled, the process of resuscitation is similar to that suggested by the Red Cross for humans – mouth to mouth – but in the case of the cat mouth to nose is better (*see 'Resuscitation'*).

LEFT
To expel water from the lungs, grasp the cat firmly by the scruff of the neck and by the rear legs and swing it downwards.

• ELECTRIC SHOCK •

INDICATIONS

Cats are notorious chewers, and the danger of electric cables means nothing to them. If your cat is electrocuted, *do not touch it until you have switched off and disconnected the appliance*, or you, too, will receive a shock.

ACTION

● Administer resuscitation as described in steps **1–3** (*see previous page*).
● Then contact the vet immediately.

• FALLS •

INDICATIONS

It is commonly thought that cats always land on their feet, but this is not necessarily so. Fractured jaws are much more common than fractured limbs after falls, and even if a cat has not actually broken or fractured bones, it may be concussed.

ACTION

● If you suspect a broken bone, get to the vet as soon as possible, restraining the cat to stop it causing itself further damage.
● There is also the possibility of internal injury which you will not be able to detect. Treat your cat for shock, and contact your vet who will advise you how to move the cat, then take it straight to the surgery.

LEFT
Cats seem to have a natural fascination for electrical gadgets, and even this seemingly inoffensive telephonel answering machine could cause a nasty shock if the cat chewed through the mains lead.

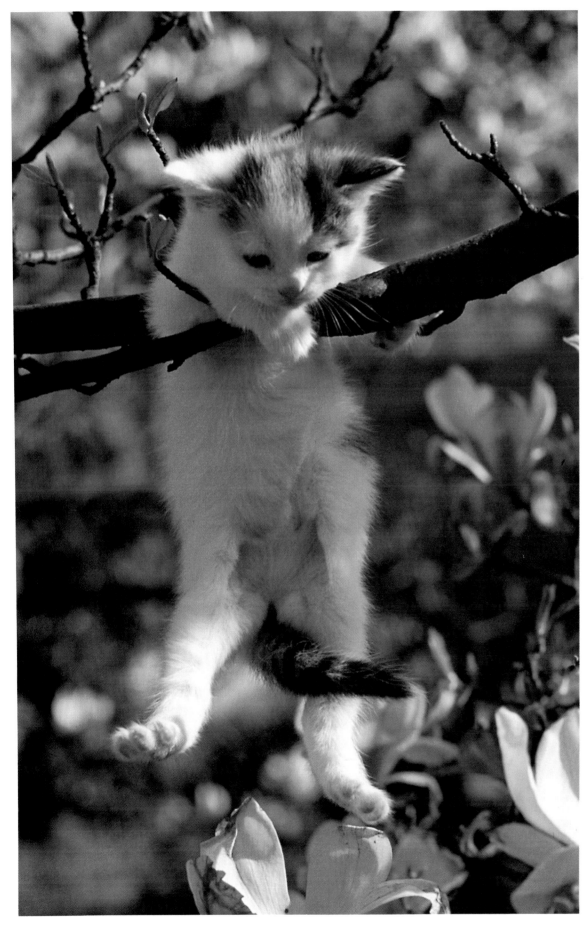

Young kittens should never be allowed outdoors unsupervised; if nobody had been at hand, this youngster could have taken a severe tumble out of the tree.

• INSECT STINGS •

INDICATIONS	ACTION
The most common stings are from wasps and bees. An external wasp sting will cause a localized inflammation. Cats love to chase flying objects and it is not unknown for them to catch and swallow wasps or bees; this may result in them being stung in the mouth or throat.	• For an external wasp sting, soothe the affected area with a cool compress. • Bees leave their sting behind in their victim, and this must be removed. If you can see the sting, pull it out with a pair of fine tweezers; if not, take the cat to the vet. • If your cat has been stung in the mouth, you must get the cat to the vet as soon as possible; the throat is liable to swell rapidly and will cause the cat to suffocate if treatment is not administered quickly. In the meantime, put a small ice cube in the cat's mouth to stop the swelling.

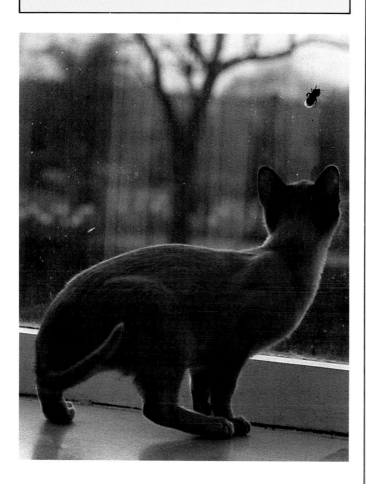

ABOVE
Cats are attracted to small flying objects, but this bee is a potential danger to the inquisitive cat.

• MINOR CUTS AND ABRASIONS •

INDICATIONS	ACTION
A small surface wound can easily be treated at home, just as you would a child's grazed knee. **BELOW** *Apply a cold compress firmly to a heavily bleeding wound. If the flow of blood does not stop after a few minutes, take the cat to the vet – the wound may need stitches.*	• Apply a little diluted antiseptic and keep a check on it in case it becomes infected. • Deeper wounds need more attention, especially if profuse bleeding occurs. • Firmly apply a cold compress directly over the wound to stem the blood flow. • If this does not stop within a few minutes, take the cat to the vet as the wound may need stitching.

• POISON •

INDICATIONS	ACTION
Poisons can get into a cat's system in two ways: ingestion (swallowing), and absorption through the paw pads.	• It is essential to get the cat to the vet as quickly as possible. • If you know what the poison is, take a sample with you as this will speed up the diagnosis and treatment. • If you know that the cat has swallowed poison, an emetic by way of a strong salt solution should be forced down the cat in order to make it vomit. • **Do not make the cat vomit if you suspect that it has swallowed a *caustic* substance, as this will cause even more damage.**

◈ ROAD ACCIDENTS ◈

INDICATIONS

Any cat that has been involved in a road accident will need urgent veterinary help and must be taken to the nearest surgery immediately. There will probably be multiple injuries to treat.

ACTION

◗ Move the injured cat as little as possible.

◗ Next to the cat, lay out a coat, blanket or whatever you have available to use as makeshift stretcher; then gently place the cat on it, moving the limbs as little as possible.

◗ Without allowing it to dangle, support the head just a little lower than the rest of the body; this will ensure that blood is still flowing to the brain and will help prevent brain damage.

◗ Keep the cat as warm and quiet as possible until you reach the surgery.

ABOVE
A cat injured in a road accident must be moved as little and as gently as possible, and it is imperative to get the accident victim to the vet as quickly as possible. A coat makes a handy stretcher; place the cat carefully on the coat and, with another person to help you, take hold of either side of the coat to lift the 'stretcher'. Support the cat's head a little lower than the rest of the body to encourage the flow of blood to the brain.

◈ SNAKE BITES ◈

INDICATIONS

In some parts of the world, snake bites are a relatively common occurrence, especially if you live in the countryside. If you do, you will be aware of the risks, and the snakes that are indigenous to your area. Many people have forgotten that there is still one venomous snake in the UK – the viper or adder.

ACTION

◗ If your cat has been bitten by a venomous snake, it is important to act fast as the venom will spread quickly through the blood system and an antiserum must be administered as soon as possible.

◗ If your vet is many miles away, the best you can do is to apply a tourniquet to restrict the blood flow, and so the spread of venom, but this should only be done as a last resort. It is extremely easy to stop the blood flow to such an extent that the tissue dies, and the limb then may have to be amputated.

◗ If the bite has come from a non-venomous snake, treat as for any other puncture wound (*see 'Animal Bites'*).

RIGHT
A cat's pulse can be checked on the inside of the upper-front legs (under the armpits).

USEFUL ADDRESSES

A list of the official organisations of the major international cat fancies, together with their official or semi-official journals.

AUSTRALIA

Co-ordinating Cat Council of Australia (CCCofA)
Box No 4317 GPO
Sydney
NSW 2001

Council of Federated Cat Clubs of Queensland
c/o Secretary
June E Lobwein
19 Clifford St
Toowoomba 4350

Feline Association of South Australia
c/o Secretary
Mr Lee Caldwell
21 Poole St
Osborne 5015

Feline Control Council of Queensland
c/o Secretary
Mrs A Barrett
84 Anzac Ave
Redcliffe 4020

Feline Control Council of Victoria (RAS)
c/o Secretary
Mrs Marion Jones
Royal Showground
Epsom Road
Ascot Vale 3032

Governing Council of the Cat Fancy in Victoria
c/o Secretary
Mrs Sandra Weaver-Hall
PO Box 73
Oakleigh 3166

Murray Valley Cat Authority
c/o Secretary
Miss Shirley E Osmond
PO Box 406
Mildura 3500

Queensland Independent Cat Council
c/o Secretary
Miss Pat Mercer
PO Box 41
Esk 4312

RNCAS Cat Club
c/o Mr Bjorn Christie-Johnston
PO Box 404
Dickson 2602

JOURNAL

Royal Agricultural Society Cat Control Journal
Box No 4317 GPO
Sydney
NSW 2001

EUROPE

Fédération Internationale Féline (FIFe)
c/o Secretary
Mme R van Haeringen
23 Doerhavelaan
Eindhoven 5644 BB
Netherlands

JOURNAL

A Tout Chat
(service des abonnements –
subscriptions)
BP 205
Versailles 78003
France

SOUTH AFRICA

Governing Council of the Associated Cat Clubs of South Africa
c/o Mrs M Simpson
45 Edison Drive
Meadowridge 7800

All Breeds Cat Club
PO Box 1078
Cape Town 8000

Cat Fanciers' Club of South Africa
PO Box 783100
Sandton 2146

Eastern Province Cat Club
PO Box 5166
Walmer 6065

Natal Cat Club
100 Marian Hill Road
Ashley
Pinetown 3610

Rand Cat Club
PO Box 180
Springs 1560

Transvaal Cat Society
PO Box 13385
Northmead 1511

Western Province Cat Club
PO Box 3600
Cape Town 8000

UNITED KINGDOM

Governing Council of the Cat Fancy (GCCF)
4–6 Penel Orlieu
Bridgewater
Somerset TA6 3PG

GCCF Cat Welfare Liaison Committee
c/o Secretary
Mrs Barbara Harrington
79 Pilgrim's Way
Kemsing
Near Sevenoaks
Kent TB15 6TD

Feline Advisory Bureau
350 Upper Richmond Road
Putney
London SW15 6TL

JOURNALS

Cats
5 James Leigh St
Manchester M1 6EX

Cat World
10 Western Road
Shoreham-by-Sea
West Sussex BN4 5WD

UNITED STATES

American Cat Association (ACA)
8101 Katherine Drive
Panorama City
CA 91402

American Cat Fanciers' Association (ACFA)
PO Box 203
Point Lookout
MO 65726

Cat Fanciers' Association (CFA Inc)
PO Box 1005
Manasquan
NJ 087361005

Cat Fanciers' Federation (CFF)
9509 Montgomery Road
Cinncinatti
OH 45242

The Independent Cat Association (TICA)
PO Box 2988
Harlingen
TX 87550

JOURNALS

Cat Fancy
PO Box 4030
San Clemente
CA 92672

Cats
445 Merrimac Drive
Port Orange
FL 32019

Cat World
PO Box 35635
Phoenix
AZ 850969

INDEX

Page numbers in *italic* refer to captions to illustrations.

ACKNOWLEDGEMENTS

My most grateful thanks to my editor LESLEY ELLIS who has helped to make this book much more readable and to JUDITH SIMONS and JOANNA LORENZ of ANNESS PUBLISHING LTD for their help and support.

ROY ROBINSON F.I.BIOL. who advised me on genetics and checked related text.

My veterinary surgeon, JOHN OLIVER B.VET.MED., MRCVS, for his advice and help in ensuring the veterinary facts are as up to date and accurate as possible.

SAL MARSH for her help on the Breeding chapter.

ROSEMARY ALGER for reading through the manuscript to check for any omissions.

BARBRO MAGNUSSON and HAZEL GLOVER for lending me their respective cats for the step-by-step grooming sequences.

LYNDA TAYLOR and the LYNCHARD CHINCHILLAS.

SUSIE MORSE for her help with the word processing.

AQUAPETS (EALING) LONDON for the loan of equipment needed for photography.

COLOUR CENTRE (LONDON) LTD for processing transparencies with their usual care and efficiency.

TERRY MOORE of the CAT SURVIVAL TRUST, Welwyn, Herts.

Lastly, my grateful thanks to my friend LYNN VAN HAEFTEN who has kindly done my shopping, errand running and kept me supplied with everything I needed while writing this book!

◆ CREDITS ◆

Photographs by Paddy Cutts, Animals Unlimited. The publishers and author would like to thank the following for additional picture material: Cat Survival Trust, page 12; E T Archives, pages 8–9; Sal Marsh, page 97; Dr K L Thoday, Royal (Dick) School of Veterinary Studies, University of Edinburgh, pages 118 *bl*, 120 *tr*; Edward Young, page 30.